Liz Strachan taught mathematics for 36 years in her home town of Montrose, Scotland. She has had over a hundred articles and short stories published and won a scholarship from the Scottish Association of Writers in 2008.

A Slice of Pi

*All the maths you forgot
to remember from school*

LIZ STRACHAN

Constable • London

Constable & Robinson Ltd
3 The Lanchesters
162 Fulham Palace Road
London W6 9ER
www.constablerobinson.com

This edition published by Constable,
an imprint of Constable & Robinson, 2009

A copy of the British Library Cataloguing in Publication
Data is available from the British Library

ISBN 978-1-84901-056-6

Printed and bound in the EU

1 3 5 7 9 10 8 6 4 2

Mixed Sources
Product group from well-managed
forests and other controlled sources
www.fsc.org Cert no. SA-COC-1565
© 1996 Forest Stewardship Council

Acknowledgements

This book wouldn't have been completed without the help
of the following wonderful people.

All my friends at Angus Writers' Circle whose constructive
criticism has always been much appreciated.

My email friend and editor, Hugh Barker, for his invaluable
guidance and vision for this book. I was so lucky to find
an editor who actually likes maths.

My darling husband, Sandy, who has
encouraged me throughout.

Contents

Introduction

When people learn that I taught maths for 36 years, they often reply, usually rather proudly, 'Oh, I hated maths when I was at school,' as if by implication, they loved and were brilliant at every other subject. I have never heard anyone admit that they hated English.

When I taught, I was determined that, whatever their ability, my pupils would come to my classroom and enjoy their maths and so become confident with it. I wanted to show them that figures can be fun and that algebra, geometry and trigonometry were for all of them, not just mysterious subjects for those with soaring IQs.

Whenever possible, I also took a few minutes to tell an anecdote about the famous mathematicians who contributed to the particular maths topic my pupils were studying. These famous mathematicians, of course, achieved so much more than school maths, and their discoveries are far beyond the comprehension of almost everyone. Their published work is the longest, densest, most esoteric material imaginable and only another mathematical genius could get excited about it. But I thought it was important for my pupils to be aware of the human side of these brilliant people. I tried to tell them that we

are where we are now, intellectually speaking, because they were there then.

We live on the mental capital accumulated by all of them. Or, as Sir Isaac Newton so eloquently put it, 'If I have been able to see further, it was only because I stood on the shoulders of giants.'

In the following pages, are many of my five-minute mathematical stories, some quirky calculations and also anecdotes from the classroom. I was always aware that I was not only teaching maths, I was also teaching teenagers who had to be encouraged, cajoled and sometimes entertained. I tried to convince them that there was more to the subject than the daily grind of simultaneous equations and factorization of quadratic expressions.

I hope that my little book will persuade a few readers to give maths another chance and perhaps some may even be converted to this most unjustly maligned of all school subjects.

CHAPTER 1

Euclid of Alexandria

(ABOUT 325–265 BC)

Almost nothing is known about the Greek mathematician Euclid, except that he must have spent most of his adult life writing *The Elements*, a great 13-volume work on geometry. It is the earliest known text on the subject and was still being taught to reluctant schoolchildren over 2,000 years after it was written.

Back in around 290 BC Ptolemy Soter, close companion to Alexander the Great, and the first king of Egypt asked Euclid to teach him some geometry. Like many who came after him, the king found the subject very difficult and asked Euclid if perhaps there was an easier way. Euclid replied, 'There are two kinds of roads, Your Majesty, roads for the common people to walk upon and roads reserved for the king only. In geometry there is no royal road.'

My pupils were lucky enough to be spared Euclidean geometry, which I had to learn at school and which many hapless youngsters continued to struggle with for quite a few years after that. Just so you know, Euclidean geometry is all to do with geometric propositions that have to be proved formally under four headings, **Given, Required, Construction, Proof.** For some reason best known to the teacher, a formidable lady widely rumoured to have webbed feet, we always had to write **QED** at the end. Certainly we would never have dared to ask. We learned later in the Latin class that it was an abbreviation for *quod erat demonstrandum* which means 'what was to be proved'. That didn't help much as none of us understood what, if anything, we had proved, and anyway, if Euclid had proved this terrible stuff all those years ago, why did we have to keep doing it? But we dutifully peppered our jotters with lots of QEDs and Miss Drake appeared to be satisfied with that.

She often used phrases like, 'Hence calculate the length of the line AB.' At age twelve, I was unfamiliar with the word 'hence', I was, however, only slightly puzzled and quite prepared to accept the fact that hens were better at Euclidean geometry than human beings.

HENS CALCULATING...

In order to pass exams, my classmates and I tried to learn these mysterious propositions by heart. This worked as long as the triangle was the original ΔABC. If the cunning examiner changed it to ΔPQR, we were well and truly stumped.

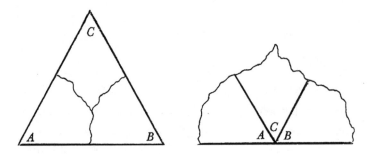

Nowadays, when teachers want to convince the class that the angles of a triangle add up to 180°, they don't resort to the mumbo-jumbo of Euclidean geometry. Each pupil is issued with a piece of scrap paper on which they draw a large triangle. They cut it out, mark the angles, A, B and C, then tear off the corners which they fit together in jigsaw puzzle fashion. Hey presto! The three angles always join up to make a straight line or 180°.

CHAPTER 2

Archimedes

(287–212 BC)

When calculating the surface area and volume of spheres, cylinders, pyramids and cones, we use formulae that were discovered by Archimedes, the Greek mathematician, over 2,000 years ago.

In the seventeenth century Newton said he was able to see ahead clearly because he was standing on the shoulders of giants. But Archimedes had to do it all on his own because there were no shoulders for him to stand on, except, perhaps, for Euclid's and his elementary geometry. But this brilliant, imaginative, original genius was not merely interested in simple geometric solids for school children.

Hiero II, the tyrant ruler of Syracuse, had given some gold to a smith to make into a crown but when it was finished, he suspected that the crown had been alloyed with other metals. He asked Archimedes to test it but the great man did not know how to do this.

A day or two later, Archimedes was in the bath house. His slave filled the tub right to the top, and when Archimedes lowered himself into the water, the rose-scented suds spilled over the edge and on to the marble tiled floor. Instead of shouting for the slave to fetch a bucket and mop, Archimedes just lay there and did some serious thinking. And what he came up with was the well-known Principle of Archimedes, which states that the apparent loss in weight of a body immersed in a liquid equals the weight of the displaced liquid.

He was so excited with his discovery that he wanted to tell everyone immediately. Forgetting about his clothes, he leapt from the bath and ran stark naked through the streets shouting 'Eureka! Eureka!' The citizens of Syracuse were very curious about what exactly their eccentric pet mathematician had found.

Back home, he now knew exactly how to determine the purity of gold. A given weight of an inferior metal is bulkier than the same weight of gold and would displace more water.

He tested the crown and it was found not to be 100 per cent gold.

History doesn't reveal what punishment the cruel Hiero devised for the cheating goldsmith, although my pupils were never short of ideas.

Archimedes didn't just sit at his desk (or in his bath) thinking about abstract ideas. He was also interested in practical problems and was a clever engineer. For example, he invented the Archimedes Screw as a method of irrigating the parched fields and vineyards of sunny Sicily. And I'm sure Archimedes would be delighted to learn that over 2,000 years

STUDYING THE SURFACE AREA OF
SPHERES AND CONES.

later, his ingenious and useful invention is still used today in places like sewage plants.

He was still an active man when he was 75. Rome was hell-bent on making Sicily part of the mighty Roman Empire and to help his adopted country fight back against the enemy fleet, he invented superbly effective weapons of war. The enemy ships were bombarded with huge boulders and balls of fire projected by enormous catapults, and grappling cranes turned over the vessels in the water and sank them.

Although he had invented the weapons, Archimedes was not there in the thick of the battle. He was engrossed in a new geometry problem when a Roman soldier came looking for him, entered his house and killed him with his sword.

CHAPTER 3

BODMAS

I f you have ever seen a teenager who is not surgically attached to a mobile phone, you must be living in Outer Mongolia.

In the maths classroom, they are equally addicted to their calculators. They have more faith in these little machines than they have in their own brains.

Take for example, $\dfrac{9 \times 7}{14 \times 3}$

Do a quick bit of cancelling and you get 1.5 in three seconds. But there will be mutterings of disagreement. 'My calculator says the answer is 13.5.' This is because they have keyed in $9 \times 7 \div 14 \times 3$. If they have only a simple calculator, they should divide the top line answer by the bottom line answer. Common sense will tell them that $63 \div 42$ could not be 13.5.

Order of calculation is all-important in maths and this is why we follow the rule of BODMAS. B stands for Brackets and has first priority, O stands for Of, D and M are Divide and

Multiply and have equal second priority and A and S are Add and Subtract which have equal third priority.

For example:

1. $4 \times (5 + 2) = 28$ (brackets first)

2. $2 + 4 \times 5 = 22$ (multiply first)

3. $5 + \frac{1}{2}$ of $6 = 8$ (of first)

4. $72 \div (12 \div 2) = 12$ (brackets first)

5. $72 \div 12 \times 4 = 24$ (no priority)

6. $26 - (2 + 3) \times 5 = 1$ (brackets first, then multiply, then subtract)

The O is of very little use, as in example 3 above, where the order of calculation is obvious. However, BODMAS is very easy to remember whereas BDMAS would be unpronounce-able, and thus doesn't work so well as a mnemonic.

CHAPTER 4

The Pythagoreans

I once taught some thirteen-year-olds to sing the Theorem of Pythagoras, 'The square on the hypotenuse of a right-angled triangle equals the sum of the squares on the other two sides.' The song was from the 1958 film *Merry Andrew* starring Danny Kaye, in which a teacher's unorthodox methods captured the imagination of his pupils.

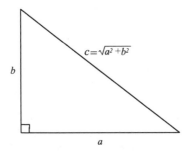

There are dozens of methods for proving the famous theorem, including the traditional Euclidean proof, but I always preferred the practical ones. The one below is easy for the children to draw especially if they are provided with squared paper.

Any right-angled triangle will do. On the largest square draw horizontal or vertical lines from the mid point of each side and rub out the extra bits.

Cut out the centre square and the four identical 'not quite' triangular pieces. The centre square fits the square on the shortest side and the remaining pieces fit jigsaw fashion into the other square.

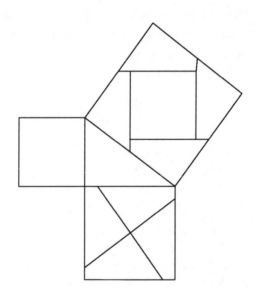

After drawing this, my pupils would fill pages in their exercise books with little problems about ladders leaning against walls and diagonal paths across rectangular fields with angry bulls in them. I also told them about the Pythagoreans.

Pythagoras, a Greek who lived from about 580 to 500 BC, founded with his wife, Theano, a school of mathematics on the Greek island of Samos. Men and women lived together in a commune, which was more like a religious order than a place of learning.

They were a mysterious, secretive lot, strict vegetarians who refused even to wear clothes made from animal skins, but also, curiously, they would not eat beans. They believed that the world could be understood through numbers, which they worshipped. All even numbers were female and earthy, odd numbers were male and divine.

2 was the first female number

3 was the first male number

4 represented justice

5 was marriage (2 + 3)

10 was the perfect number which they especially revered.

They also loved geometric shapes, but in spite of the triangles and squares which would make Pythagoras famous to the end

FEMALE AND MALE NUMBERS

of time, it was the magical five-pointed-star shape, the pentagram, that they admired most. His favourite solid was the sphere which he thought was perfect and on that basis alone, he and his followers believed the world was round. Because in their minds, the gods who created the earth would not have chosen any other shape.

However, for a while, there was trouble brewing in the commune. One of the members, a mathematician called Hipassus, made a discovery which upset them all. In a right-angled triangle whose shorter sides are one unit long, the hypotenuse is $\sqrt{2}$ and try as he might, he could not get an exact answer for this. Eventually, Hipassus had to admit his fears that there were some numbers which could not be evaluated exactly. Actually, what he had done was discover irrational numbers.

The other Pythagoreans were angry. They could not accept the existence of such numbers and Hipassus's announcement was looked on as absolute heresy. Legend has it that the poor man was expelled from the commune. Later, to ensure his silence, they tied weights to his legs and threw him in the sea.

My pupils didn't think much of the Pythagoreans, and when they found out that the Babylonians knew about the right-angled triangle and the squares on its sides over a thousand years before, they accused him of plagiarism. In fact, the only part of this story that always fascinated my pupils was the ban on beans and they had some colourful ideas as to why this might have been so.

One of my boys summed up the Pythagoreans perfectly. 'Miss,' he said, 'I think the whole lot of them were two degrees short of a right angle.'

CHAPTER 5

Pierre de Fermat

(1601–65)

There is an infinite number of values for a, b, c for which $a^2 + b^2 = c^2$, known as the Pythagorean triples, for example (3 4 5), (5 12 13), and (9 40 41).

Fermat, a French lawyer and government official, was also an enthusiastic mathematician, and in 1640 he wrote a statement in the margin of his favourite maths book, *Arithmetica* by Diophantus, a Greek mathematician of the third century. Fermat said he was certain that a solution to $a^n + b^n = c^n$ did not exist for any values of n greater than 2. For example, there was no solution for $a^3 + b^3 = c^3$ or $a^4 + b^4 = c^4$. And what's more, he said, he could prove it. However, the maths book was not discovered until after his death and although the mathematical statement was there in the margin, the proof was missing.

This was called Fermat's Last Theorem, and as theorems go, Fermat's one was pretty boring. You would have thought that no one would care a jot whether it was proved or not. Wrong! Mathematicians thought it was the most tantalizing marginal note in the history of the subject and they worked at the problem for 370 years without success. Fermat's Last Theorem has the reputation of being the mathematical problem with the greatest number of published incorrect proofs. But at last, in 1995, a British mathematician called Sir Andrew Wiles, now a professor at Princeton University, published a proof that has not been disputed.

The news of the elusive proof spread throughout the world, getting more public acclamation from the maths community than even the first moon landing.

CHAPTER 6

The Baker's Dozen

One might imagine that the baker's dozen was the medieval equivalent of today's BOGOF offers in the supermarkets. But 'buy one, get one free' has no other purpose than to tempt the customer into the store where they will buy the BOGOF bargains but also spend another £20 on other things and thereby increase supermarket profits. Getting an extra loaf of bread when only twelve were ordered originally happened for a very different reason.

An early English statute during the reign of Henry III, who was king for a very long time between 1216 and 1272, ruled that if a baker cheated his customer by giving him short measure, he would pay dearly for his crime. The punishment was at best a fine, but more likely a flogging or several hours in the pillory where the offender was imprisoned in a wooden frame with holes for his head and hands. Pillories were situated in the most frequented places and the prisoner was exposed to the bloodthirsty crowds who took great delight in throwing things and torturing him.

To ensure that he didn't accidentally give short measure,

the law abiding baker always threw in an extra loaf and this practice was called the baker's dozen even though fewer loaves than a dozen were ordered. For a smaller purchase, the baker always added at least an extra piece of stale bread.

Modern day bakers no longer fear these barbarous laws and bakeries today have equipment to check that the product is of a uniform size. A version of the baker's dozen is still in operation in some shops but like the BOGOFs in the supermarkets, it's to encourage the customer to come back, not to avoid violent retribution

CHAPTER 7

Divisibility by 3

Three friends win £718452 in the National Lottery. Panic! Will this enormous figure divide by three exactly?

Quick check: If they add up the digits, they would find that they make 27, which is on the three times table, so they can relax while, if necessary, they hunt for a calculator to work out each share.

Another three friends have only four winning numbers and collect £172 whose digits add up to 10, which is *not* on the three times table.

With the left over £1 they decide to buy another Lottery ticket.

A similar divisibility test works for six and nine but for six, not only do the digits have to add up to a number on the six times table, the original number has to be even.

For example, which of the following work out exactly?

1. $15\,312 \div 6$? Yes, the number is even and the sum of the digits is 12, which is on the six times table.

2. $421\,641 \div 6$? No, although the sum of the digits is 18, which is on the six times table, the original number is not even.

3. $669\,375 \div 9$? Yes, the digits add to 36 which is on the nine times table.

There are many other divisibility tests. If you need to know if a number is divisible by 7 this is what you do.

Does $5\,292$ divide by 7?

Double the last digit and subtract it from 529 giving 525. Again double the last digit and subtract it from 52 giving 42 which is on the seven times table so $5\,292$ is divisible by 7.

But it would have been quicker to do the original division as is the case for all the others.

CHAPTER 8

Rough Is Enough

I f, for some obscure reason, you need to work out 83 per cent of £147.25, for goodness sake, use a calculator. Key in 147.25 × 83% (do NOT press the = button) Answer £122.22.

For 'out and about' percentages, in shops, restaurants and everyday conversation, **rough is enough.** This is how it works:

To calculate 10 per cent of a sum of money, forget about the pence, and drop the last figure in the £s.

For example:

1. 10% of £83.27, first discard the 27p, then drop the 3. So 10% is £8 (approx)

2. 10% of £2 004 is £200 (approx)

3. 10% of £499 (call it £500) is £50 (approx)

And from 10% you can calculate other commonly used percentages like 20% and 5%.

The VAT rate (the UK sales tax) is 17.5% (a nasty looking

number) – but it is not impossible to work out any sales tax of 17.5% in your head. Honest!

17.5% = 10% + 5% + 2.5%. Let's say you are about to buy a new computer. The conversation may go rather like this:

Manager:	This is our special 'today only' offer, never to be repeated. Just £799.
You:	Does that include VAT?
Manager:	No, unfortunately that will be an extra 17½%, sir.
You:	Oh, call it £800, so 10% is £80, 5% is £40 and 2½% is £20. That's an extra £140! (preparing to walk away)
Manager:	(laying down his calculator) Would a total of £850 be acceptable, sir?
You:	Make it £830 and we have a deal.

Tipping

In Britain, tipping is very much a casual calculation. For a taxi fare of £4, you would probably hand over a fiver, and tell the cabbie to keep the change. But for a longer journey costing £14, you would still probably give the driver an extra £1. A restaurant bill of £92.40 would be rounded up to £100 and if you get a bad haircut, you don't leave any tip at all.

It's a different matter in the USA where rough is definitely not enough, and a minimum of 15 per cent is expected and 20 per cent is hoped for. If you leave less, make sure you have a fast car with its engine running just outside the door. A restaurant bill for four people in New York might be $141.98. Using the **rough is enough** rule, drop the cents, 10 per cent is $14 so 5 per cent is $7, adding to $21. So what about leaving a $20 bill?

Better make it $25 if you ever want to go near the place again.

CHAPTER 9

Don't be Fooled

Beware of politicians who talk in percentages. There is usually some underhand reason why they prefer not to use simple figures.

> **Politician:** We are offering student nurses a huge 10 per cent rise in their annual salaries. This year, we are settling for a modest 2 per cent rise in our own salaries.

Well, 10% of £12 000 is £1 200 and 2% of £120 000 is double that.

There are lies, damned lies and politicians' percentages.

CHAPTER 10

A Percentage Puzzle

opey Donald is telling his chum, Brainy Brian, that he has just sold two old computer games on eBay. The first one he sold for £12, which his mum said was a 25 per cent loss on what he had paid for it. He sold the second one, also for £12, but this time his mum said this was a 25 per cent profit on what he had paid for it.

'So,' said Dopey Donald, 'I broke even.'

'No you didn't,' said Brainy Brian who was a whizz kid at all things mathematical and in particular, percentages. 'Here are my calculations.'

Game 1
Selling Price = £12
Loss = 25%
75% is therefore £12
So 100% is £12 × $^{100}/_{75}$ = £16
Actual loss = £4

Game 2
Selling Price = £12
Profit = 25%
125% is therefore £12
So 100% is £12 × $^{100}/_{125}$ = £9.60
Actual Gain = £2.40

'So you really made an overall loss of £1.60.'

But poor Donald's eyes had long since glazed over.

CHAPTER 11

Percentage Up and Percentage Down

(A Cautionary Tale)

I n 2007, young Andy Morris thought that living with Mum was restricting his social life so he decided it was time to leave home and buy a brand new flat.

With no savings at all, he nevertheless had no trouble in securing a 100 per cent mortgage of £150 000. After all, he was a bank clerk and a job in a bank was as safe as … well, as safe as houses.

Life was wonderful. In April 2008, he learned that the value of flats like his had increased by 20 per cent. What's more, his bank bonus was very generous and he bought a second hand Porsche.

His flat was now worth £150 000 + 20% of £150 000. Pressing a few buttons on his calculator, he was delighted to see that this was £180 000. Wow! Just think what it would be worth the next year.

But in January 2009, bad things were happening in banks

and Andy lost his job. He tried to sell his flat for £180 000 but house prices had now plummeted by 20 per cent.

'Back to square one,' thought Andy, whose arithmetic, for a bank clerk, was somewhat suspect. His Mum did a quick calculation in her head, 'That's £180 000 – 20% of £180 000. Let's see, that's £180 000 – £36 000. Oh, Andy, that's only £144 000. You're in negative equity.'

And to make matters worse, nobody wanted to buy his car.

Luckily, he was able to go back home to live with his mum.

CHAPTER 12

Compound Interest

I refuse to admit that any school maths topic is boring. Take compound interest, for instance. The text book will probably have a worked example about a man who invests £200 at 5 per cent per annum and leaves it there in the bank for 3 years. Who could get excited about the £232 (approx.) he has accumulated?

But money *is* exciting so my class and I would discuss a few well known quotations about the subject before we started any calculations.

1. Money talks.

2. Money makes money.

3. Unto every one that hath, shall more be given and he shall have abundance. (Matthew 25:29)

4. Neither a borrower nor a lender be. (Hamlet)

5. Money is the root of all evil.

6. Dirty money.

7. Throw good money after bad.

Then imagine that batty, multi-millionaire Great-Aunt Marilla leaves everyone in the class £2 104 237 in her will. I allow them to spend the odd £104 237 on anything they want but they have to invest the £2 million at 5 per cent for 3 years.

Year I   Interest on £2 000 000 at 5% = £100 000

            Investment after 1 year = £2 100 000

Year II   Interest on £2 100 000 at 5% = £105 000

            Investment after 2 years = £2 205 000

Year III   Interest on £2 205 000 at 5% = £110 250

            Investment after 3 years = £2 315 250

This is certainly an example of money making money and 'to him who hath shall more be given'.

Later, they learn the formula for compound interest,

$$A = P(1 + {}^{r}\!/_{100})^{t}$$

In the formula A is the amount accumulated at the end of the investment period, P is the Principal or the money put into the bank originally, r is the rate % and t is the time in years.

For the above investment:

$$A = 2\,000\,000(1 + \tfrac{5}{100})^3$$

$$= 2\,000\,000(1.05)^3$$

$$= 2\,000\,000 \times 1.157625$$

$$= \pounds2\,315\,250$$

With a scientific calculator, my class could do the whole calculation with the press of a few buttons. This way they could see exactly how rich they were going to become, in imaginary money, at least.

CHAPTER 13

How Times Have Changed

I have a very old book called *Real Life Arithmetic for Girls* by Olive Morgan. In the preface the author writes:

> The average girl will not be much interested in mathematics. It is advisable, however, that she is able to add together sums of money so that she can check the bill in a teashop and present accurate household accounts to her husband.

In the same book, the girl is encouraged to use a ruler accurately by making a paper pattern for a pair of knickers. The instructions read,

> Measure the full height of the person for whom the garment is intended. The length of the knickers will be seven sixteenths of this height in a normal person. The width will be three and three quarter times the length.

It is hard to believe that any teenager, even one in those unenlightened days, would have considered making that truly scary garment with double French seams in places to cause permanent injury. Hopefully, it never got beyond the paper pattern stage.

My girls were outraged. If they had ever got their hands on the author, she would have been lynched. Although, on further reflection, we remembered that the Second World War was only a few years away from the book's original publication and decided that Ms Morgan had been helping the war effort.

These voluminous megabloomers would no doubt have made pretty effective parachutes.

CHAPTER 14

Karl Friedrich Gauss

(1777–1855)

The story of Karl Friedrich Gauss is a fascinating one. Born in Brunswick, Germany, he was the only child of poor peasants and lived in miserable conditions. However, they struggled to pay for some elementary education for their son and so began the career of one of the greatest mathematicians of all time.

Most of Gauss's work can be understood only by other brilliant mathematicians, but there is one story which always captivates people's interest.

When Gauss was ten, he and his classmates were instructed to add up all the numbers from 1 to 100. Their teacher, Herr Buttner, was tired and thought that this task would keep the class quietly occupied for the rest of the afternoon. After five seconds, Gauss raised his hand and said, 'The answer is 5050, sir.'

Gauss had invented the formula N × (N + 1) ÷ 2 so he had quickly multiplied 100 by 101, then divided by 2 getting 5050 for the total of the numbers from 1 to 100.

Go on, try a few examples for yourself:

1. $1 + 2 + 3 + 4 + 5 = 15$

    or $5 \times 6 \div 2 = 15$

2. $1 + 2 + 3 + 4 + 5 + 6 + 7 + 8 + 9 + 10 = 55$
    or $10 \times 11 \div 2 = 55$

There is another version of the story. It wasn't Herr Buttner who wanted to have a little nap while his class slaved over their boring sum, it was young Gauss. Noticing Gauss's head nodding on to the desk, the teacher tiptoed up to the boy. He saw a few figures scratched out on his slate, '$1 + 100 = 101, 2 + 99 = 101, 3 + 98 = 101, 4 + 97 = 101$ etc. There are 50 pairs of numbers whose sum is 101, so the answer is $101 \times 50 = 5050$.' At this point, Gauss had got bored waiting for his classmates to finish and had closed his eyes.

Whatever maths Gauss used, our little brain of Germany was not popular with his teacher that afternoon, but Herr Buttner recognized the boy's genius and arranged for sponsors to finance all his future education.

CHAPTER 15

A Little More Gauss

Triangular numbers do what you would expect: They can be arranged in triangles.

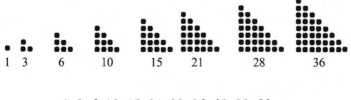

or 1 3 6 10 15 21 28 36 45 55 66 etc

Since each triangular number is made up of 1 + 2 + 3 + 4 + ... spots, using Gauss's N × (N + 1) ÷ 2 formula, you can find any number along the line.

The 36th triangular number is 36 × 37 ÷ 2 = 666 which is one of the symbols for the Devil and is referred to in the Bible (Revelations 13) as the number of the beast. In *The Phantom of the Opera* there is more scary stuff – 666 was the lot number at auction of the huge chandelier which crashed to the floor of the Paris Opera House.

Gauss proved that any non triangular number was the sum of two or three triangular numbers.

For example:

1. 32 = 21 + 10 + 1
2. 60 = 45 + 15
3. 13 = 10 + 3

But how on earth did he manage to prove it for *all* numbers? Was this what he was doing when the doctor ran to Gauss's study to inform him that Frau Gauss was dying? The mathematician replied, 'Tell my dear wife to hang on a little longer. I'm in the middle of solving a rather difficult problem.'

Gauss was regarded as such a genius that after his death, his brain was removed for neurological research; as was Einstein's after his death in 1955.

2+2 = er... um... Maybe I can't do it because my brain has been removed... Or maybe because I'm dead.

CHAPTER 16

Temperatures

The British public have not quite made up their minds whether they want the temperature to be measured in degrees Fahrenheit or Centigrade. Helpful television weather forecasters give us both. 'In the north east of Scotland, temperatures are expected to fall to 25 degrees Fahrenheit, that's a very cold minus 4 degrees Centigrade.' In the USA, no one talks Centigrade.

To change °C to °F, divide by 5, multiply by 9 and add 32.

For example, 100°C = (100 ÷ 5 × 9) + 32 = 212°F.

To change °F to °C, do the opposite. Subtract 32, divide by 9 and multiply by 5.

For example, (95°F = (95 − 32) ÷9 × 5 = 35°C

Two easy ones to remember are:

$$16°C = 61°F$$

and

$$28°C = 82°F$$

And not many people know this! It may help you win the pub quiz one day.

$-40°C$ is exactly the same temperature as $-40°F$

CHAPTER 17

The Missing £10

Three businessmen travelling home after a conference were alarmed by the deteriorating weather conditions. They were lucky to get the last available room in a nearby hotel.

The manager charged £120 for the night, but as they weren't staying for breakfast and the room was shabby, he decided later to give them a refund of £20. The porter on his way up to the room with four £5 notes calculated that £20 would not divide exactly by 3 so he pocketed one of the notes.

Now the businessmen had paid £105 for the room, the porter had £5 in his pocket, making £110 altogether.

Hold on! What happened to the other £10?

Normally this was an end of lesson little puzzle and I would ask for an explanation the following day.

If you want more time to think about it, ignore the explanation below.

Answer: The £105 and the £5 shouldn't be added. Subtract instead getting £100. The men paid £105, the hotel got £100 and the porter took £5 so it all balances very nicely.

Chapter 18

Sin, Cos and Tan

The history of trigonometry goes back to the earliest recorded mathematics in Egypt and Babylon where it was used to aid navigation. Hipparchus of Greece took the subject a step further, but it was the sixth-century Indian mathematician, Aryabhata who laid down a basis for trigonometry by developing tables of sines and cosines.

Trigonometry is usually shortened to trig, and the trig ratios of Sine, Cosine and Tangent shortened to Sin, Cos and Tan. Teenagers, for reasons that I have never understood, seem to take to trigonometry like a dot to a decimal. Maybe it's because it gives them a certain feeling of one-upmanship in the family as often this is the age when most parents give up trying to help their clever offspring with their maths homework. 'What on earth is that sin cos tan stuff all about?' they would ask at the Parents' Evening. 'Jaimie has no problem with it, though,' they would add, thinking perhaps that they had produced a mathematical genius.

Well, at the beginning, what it is all about is the right-angled triangle and the relationship between the sides and the angles.

We always started with the tan ratio and immediately we put the new knowledge into action. Armed with plastic clinometers, tape measures and jotters, our aim was to measure the height of the Old Kirk steeple which has been, for centuries, a welcome landmark for all homecoming Montrosians.

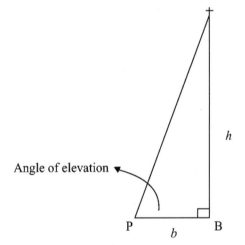

We measured a line from the base of the building to point P. Then from P we aimed the clinometer like a gun at the top of the steeple and recorded the angle of elevation.

$$\text{Tan } P° = \frac{h}{b}$$

and so we calculated the height (h)

If the High Street was busy, we would have too many interested spectators who already knew that the height of the steeple was about 220 feet.

The other ratios are:

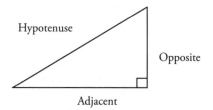

Sin = **O**pposite ÷ **H**ypotenuse

Cos = **A**djacent ÷ **H**ypotenuse

Tan = **O**pposite ÷ **A**djacent

giving the mnemonic

SOH CAH TOA

The boys used to chant SOH CAH TOA in what they imagined was a Chinese accent.

CHAPTER 19

A Number Trick Using a Little Bit of Algebra

Algebra was invented by a little known Arabian mathematician called Al Khwarizmi. His book called *Al Jabr* (the science of equations) gave a name to this branch of maths.

Algebra is like arithmetic but uses letters and symbols to represent numbers and form equations to solve problems. I always had to work hard to convince my pupils how much they enjoyed algebra and that there is nothing better for the soul than solving a tricky little equation.

Simple number tricks where you say, 'Think of a number and I'll tell you what it is,' are always done by algebra.

For example:

1. Think of a number between 1 and 10

2. Multiply it by 5

3. Add 7

4. Multiply by 2

5. Add any other number between 1 and 10

6. Subtract 3

7. Ask for the final answer.

8. Do a spot of accurate mind reading.

In Algebra, this is

1. x

2. $5x$

3. $5x + 7$

4. $(5x + 7) \times 2 = 10x + 14$

5. $10x + 14 + y$

7. $10x + 11 + y$

So if the final answer is, say, 73, you then do a simple equation,

$10x + 11 + y = 73$

Subtract 11 from both sides of the equation, giving
$10x + y = 62$

10 times 'what?' + 'what?' would give 62?

So, the first number must be 6 and the other number added on must be 2

The more you try it, the easier it gets. I promise.

CHAPTER 20

Numbers Connecting with Algebra

Take, for example, $5^2 = 25$. Now multiply the numbers before and after 5 giving $4 \times 6 = 24$
Do the same for some other squares.

$$10^2 = 100 \text{ and } 9 \times 11 = 99$$

$$15^2 = 225 \text{ and } 14 \times 16 = 224$$

$$20^2 = 400 \text{ and } 19 \times 21 = 399$$

$$55^2 = 3\,025 \text{ and } 54 \times 56 = 3\,024$$

$$748^2 = 559\,504 \text{ and } 747 \times 749 = 559\,503$$

But does this work for *all* numbers? Or will some famous mathematician spend a lifetime proving it?

Not this time. Every 14-year-old pupil at school knows that

$$x^2 - 1 = (x - 1)(x + 1)$$

CHAPTER 21

The National Lottery

Sometimes, at school, I used to get requests from home. For example, 'My Dad wants to know how to work out the chance of winning the jackpot in the Lottery.'

First, I drew the attention of the class to a button on their calculators which appeared to have a letter with an exclamation mark on it, **n!** This does *not* mean 'Wow! It's that letter n again' or, 'n? I can't believe it!'

It means factorial n. For example, 6! means $6 \times 5 \times 4 \times 3 \times 2 \times 1$ and 100! means $100 \times 99 \times 98 \times 97 \times 96 \times \ldots$ and so on, finishing with $5 \times 4 \times 3 \times 2 \times 1$ and this huge multiplication would give a very large answer indeed.

To work out the chance of getting all six winning numbers from the possible forty-nine numbers you work out $^{49}C_6$.

Which means 49!, ÷ (6! × 43!)

$$= (49×48×47×46×45 \dots × 1)$$
$$÷ (6×5×4×3×2×1 × 43×42×41×40×39 \dots ×1)$$

and that all cancels down nicely to
(49×48×47×46×45×44) ÷ 720, giving
13 983 816

So the chance of winning the jackpot is roughly **1 in 14 million**.

One can but dream.

CHAPTER 22

Binary Numbers

The binary system, where any number can be written using only the digits 1 and 0, was invented by the great German mathematician, **Gottfried Wilhelm Leibniz** (1646–1716). Leibniz was a very religious man and he associated 1 with God and 0 with nothingness and it pleased him that all numbers could be created out of unity and nothing.

At the time, his invention seemed to have no practical use whatsoever. But now, most computing devices use this number system because computer memory is made up of small elements which can only be in two states, off/on or 0/1.

Teenagers seem to find the binary system easy to learn. This is how it works:

Try to remember how you started to count. We used to have headings like this:

←	←	**Hundreds**	**Tens**	**Units**
		7	4	2

so 7 × 100 = 700, 4 × 10 = 40 and 2 × 1 = 2, giving 742

The headings for Binary Numbers are:

← ← Sixteens Eights Fours Twos Units

So take the number 15, for example. This is 8 + 4 + 2 + 1 so *one* lot of each of these goes under the appropriate headings giving the binary number 1111.

Now take 22. This is 16 + 4 + 2. Put these under the appropriate headings remembering to fill in the missing headings with 0 and you get the binary number 10110.

The headings, of course, can be extended as far as you need, by doubling the previous heading.

Changing back from binary to decimal is even easier. 1110001 (using the headings) give 1 × 64, 1 × 32, 1 × 16, 0 × 8, 0 × 4, 0 × 2, 1 × 1 = **113**.

My class then used to enjoy the rest of the lesson writing the numbers 1 to 26 in binary notation and writing secret code messages.

		Binary number			Binary number
A	1	1	N	14	1110
B	2	10	O	15	1111
C	3	11	P	16	10000
D	4	100	Q	17	10001
E	5	101	R	18	10010
F	6	110	S	19	10011
G	7	111	T	20	10100
H	8	1000	U	21	10101
I	9	1001	V	22	10110
J	10	1010	W	23	10111
K	11	1011	X	24	11000
L	12	1100	Y	25	11001
M	13	1101	Z	26	11010

One personal message read:

10 1001 1100 1100 11001 /// 1100 1111
10110 101 10011 /// 1010 101 1110 1110
11001

CHAPTER 23

Knockout Competitions

S ports club secretaries who have to organize knockout competitions love the binary headings:

| 1 | 2 | 4 | 8 | 16 | 32 | 64 |

which can be written

| 2^0 | 2^1 | 2^2 | 2^3 | 2^4 | 2^5 | 2^6 |

They particularly like 16 (2^4). The names of 16 competitors are drawn out of the hat in pairs. They play the first round, the 8 winners play the second round, then there is the semi-final followed by the exciting final which results in the proud champion receiving the Doris Mills-Dutton silver rose bowl.

Unfortunately, golfers, tennis players and bowlers do not write their names on the competition lists in neat convenient powers of 2.

Suppose there are 13 names or 18 names?

In the first case, subtract 13 from the next power of 2 (16).

16–13 = 3, so 3 lucky players get a bye into the second round. The other 10 competitors play in the first round and the 5 winners go forward to meet the 3 byes and then the competition progresses as before.

For 18 competitors, subtract 18 from the next power of 2. (32) 32 – 18 = 14 so this time 14 players get a bye into the second round and only 4 (18 – 14) have to play in the first round. The two winners join the other 14, making 16 in the second round and the competition continues to the final.

However, a club secretary doesn't need to worry about these calculations. They usually have a table passed down from previous officials which might look something like this (overleaf):

Number of competitors	Number in Round 1	Number of byes
8	8	0
9	2	7
10	4	6
11	6	5
12	8	4
13	10	3
14	12	2
15	14	1
16	16	0
17	2	15
18	4	14
19	6	13
20	8	12

So a competition secretary doesn't need to be a mathematical genius. But it does impress the other committee members if he or she can calculate the byes in their head.

CHAPTER 24

Angels and Angelina

I could bet on it. In every first year maths test, one of the little 12-year-old darlings would write:

'In Δ ABC, ∠ BAC is a cute angel.'

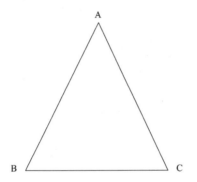

Over the years, I taught several girls whose name was Angela and, for one memorable year, a girl called Angelina. Poor Angelina could not have been described as a cute angel.

There are 647 recorded excuses for not doing maths homework and Angelina and her mum knew every one of them. On crumpled notes, usually on paper torn out of the maths exercise book, Mrs Stewart would keep me up-to-date with the family health.

'Dear miss, sorry Angelina missed her maths test. I have been under the doctor with my leg and I needed Angelina to look after Henrietta-May.'

'Dear miss, Angelina vomited up the High Street at dinner time so she couldn't hand in her homework.'

'Dear miss, Angelina had ~~diarhor~~, ~~diahorr~~ loose bowls all during EastEnders and didn't manage to do her algebra.'

AN ANGLE
ANGEL

CHAPTER 25

An Easy Maths Trick

Write down a two digit number whose digits are not the same, reverse the digits and take the smaller number from the bigger one. Reverse the digits again and add the two numbers. The answer is always 99.

Examples:

72

<u>27</u>

45

<u>54</u>

99

and

40

<u>04</u>

36

<u>63</u>

99

and

98

<u>89</u>

09

<u>90</u>

99

This trick also works for three digit numbers, for example 641, and the final answer is always 1089.

CHAPTER 26

A Quick Way to Multiply by 11

By the following method, multiplying even a large number by 11 only takes a few seconds. For example:

$$724361 \times 11$$

Write down the first and last digits with a space in between,

$$7 \qquad 1$$

Now add the digits in pairs from right to left,

$$1 + 6 = 7$$

$$6 + 3 = 9$$

$$3 + 4 = 7$$

$$4 + 2 = 6$$

$$2 + 7 = 9$$

Now fill in 96797 in the space.

Answer 7967971

You have to work from right to left because if the pair of digits adds to more than 9, for example 6 + 8 = 14, you have to write down the 4 and carry 1.

Easy!

CHAPTER 27

Eratosthenes

(276–194 BC)

A small part of the work of the Greek mathematician Eratosthenes was studied by my 12-year-olds. They used The Sieve of Eratosthenes to discover all the prime numbers from 1 to 100. A prime number has no divisors other than itself and 1. For example, 13 only divides by 13 and 1

On squared paper, they wrote down the numbers on a 10 by 10 grid and with coloured pencils systematically sieved out all the non prime numbers, starting with 1. Then, leaving 2 which is the only even prime, they eliminated all the other even numbers, then the multiples of 3, 5 and 7 and so on until only the prime numbers were left.

The 25 prime numbers between 1 and 100 are:

2 3 5 7 11 13 17 19 23 29 31 37 41 43 47 53 59 61 67
71 73 79 83 89 97.

Apart from the first two prime numbers, 2 and 3, it is thought that all prime numbers are of the form **6n + 1** or **6n − 1** where n is any number.

For example $6 \times 5 - 1 = 29$ which is prime and $6 \times 151 + 1 = 907$ which is also prime. But since no one has proved that the prime numbers go on for ever, these ultra-cautious sticklers for supreme accuracy will never say that the formula works for all prime numbers.

Not only was Eratosthenes a fine mathematician, he was also a poet, an athlete, an astronomer and a geographer, but despite all his achievements, he was nicknamed 'Beta' (the second letter in the Greek alphabet) by his contemporaries. The 'alpha' mathematician was, of course, his older friend and mentor, Archimedes.

Like other mathematicians in ancient Greece, Eratosthenes had a bash at calculating the circumference of the earth. He came up with 250 000 stadia. The problem is that a stadion (plural stadia) is the length of a stadium. The Greeks loved their chariot racing and there were stadiums of different lengths all over the place. However, if Eratosthenes used 1 stadion = 160 metres, then he was almost spot on!

$$250\,000 \times 160 \div 1\,000 = 40\,000 \text{ km}$$

He came to a sad end, however. He became blind in his old age and because he could not see to do his beloved mathematics, he starved himself to death.

He would have been proud to learn that hundreds of years later, a large, deep crater in the moon was named Eratosthenes Crater to honour his work in astronomy.

CHAPTER 28

Christian Goldbach

(1690–1764)

S ome mathematicians, according to my pupils, should get themselves a proper job and stop fretting about trivial problems that seem to have no practical value.

Take, for instance, prime numbers. We've looked at the first 25 prime numbers found by the Sieve of Eratosthenes, but they go on for ever. Or do they? Maybe there is a point on the number line beyond which there are no more prime numbers. This is a mystery which mathematicians have not yet solved.

Christian Goldbach was a Russian mathematician who had many interests other than numbers. In fact, he has been accused of treating maths as a recreation. Not taking maths seriously? Just how irresponsible is that!

As a young man he travelled widely in Europe returning home to be Professor of Mathematics at the University of St Petersburg. Soon after, Peter II became Czar of Russia, and since he was only eleven-years-old, he needed a tutor so Goldbach took over this job until his young pupil died of smallpox, three years later. However, Goldbach remained at court taking on more and more important roles in the government of Russia.

He still dabbled in maths, however, and in 1742 he wrote to his good friend and fellow mathematician Leonhard Euler in Switzerland asking for his help with a problem that came to be known as Goldbach's Conjecture. He thought that every even number over 2 could be expressed as the sum of two prime numbers. It's easy to give examples:

$$4 = 2 + 2$$

$$8 = 5 + 3$$

$$16 = 11 + 5$$

$$50 = 47 + 3$$

$$1000 = 983 + 17$$

etc. etc.

But neither man could prove that this was true for *all* even numbers.

It has been checked in recent years by computer and in the millions of even numbers tested not one has failed to be the sum of two prime numbers.

Ordinary mortals would think that is proof enough. But it hasn't been proved for *all* numbers so Goldbach's Conjecture remains just that … a mere conjecture.

CHAPTER 29

Handshakes

I used to play bowls, as well as golf, but I gave up the former for two reasons. First, there was a champion bowler in the town who had the same surname as me. Her name was in the local paper every week for winning some competition or another. My pupils thought this woman was me and they were mightily impressed. Then she died suddenly and my reputation as a bowler died too. Secondly, bad shots in bowls are played in full view of everyone on the green and in the clubhouse. But out there on the golf course, the good, the bad and the ugly mostly go unnoticed. I much prefer my golf. Like all golfers, I can always find excuses for a bad shot, like 'The wind blew my eyelashes' or 'The sun went behind a cloud.'

In a bowls match, before they start playing, both teams, each consisting of the lead, second, third and skip shake hands with everybody saying, 'Have a nice game,' which is a bit of a joke since obviously you really want the opposition to have a rotten game.

With eight people playing altogether on each team, how many handshakes are there before the game gets under way?

HAND AND FOOT SHAKING

Player A shakes hands with B, C, D, E, F, G, H

Player B with C, D, E, F, G, H

Player C with D, E, F, G, H

Player D with E, F, G, H

Player E with F, G, H

Player F with G, H

Player G with H

This is a total of 28 handshakes. Again we see that 28 is a triangular number and instead of adding, the answer can be calculated as in the previous page, $7 \times 8 \div 2 = 28$.

If Scotland were playing England in the football World Cup Final and they decided to do this handshaking palaver, there would be

21 x 22 ÷ 2 = 231 handshakes.

I know one thing for certain; they wouldn't be hoping the opposing side was going to have a nice game!

CHAPTER 30

Exploring the Magic of Numbers

I n the early 1990s, computers started to appear in the maths classrooms. Correction! A single 14-inch screen computer, accompanied by a thousand or so page user guide, was donated by the Parent Teacher Association. It sat on a surplus desk ignored by me for many weeks.

Nowadays, almost every child has access to a computer, but in those early years there were very few around. Although I didn't want to have anything to do with computers, my pupils certainly did. They appeared at 8.30am, break time, lunch time and queued impatiently to have a go on the new machine.

Gradually, and reluctantly, I allowed myself to be converted from a sad old Luddite to the computer addict that I am today.

We could now do calculations like the ones below, which were previously terminally tedious or even impossible to do with pencil and paper.

$$1 \times 1 = 1$$

$$11 \times 11 = 121$$

$$111 \times 111 = 12321$$

$$1111 \times 1111 = 1234321$$

$$11111 \times 11111 = 123454321$$

$$111111 \times 111111 = 12345654321$$

$$1111111 \times 1111111 = 1234567654321$$

$$11111111 \times 11111111 = 123456787654321$$

$$111111111 \times 111111111 = 12345678987654321$$

One of the class said this pattern reminded her of the old nursery rhyme,

> The Grand Old Duke of York
> He had ten thousand men
> He marched them up to the top of the hill
> And he marched them down again.

So we displayed 'The Grand Old Duke of York' pattern on the wall with all their other work.

But when they keyed in

$$1111111111 \times 1111111111$$

and got the answer $1\,234\,567\,900\,987\,654\,321$, the class was disappointed. Where is the 8? It is missing between the 7 and 9 and the eleven digit version and all the ones to follow in the pattern are also missing the 8, although the centre part begins to form a new pattern of its own.

But the class had simultaneous equations awaiting them, so we decided to leave 'The Grand Old Duke of York' pattern for some modern day Goldbach to concern himself about.

CHAPTER 31

Squares You Can Do in Your Head

There's a little bit of one-upmanship in being able to do sums in your head. In these squares, we cheated a little.

$$15^2 = 15 \times 15 = 225$$

$$25^2 = 25 \times 25 = 625$$

$$35^2 = 35 \times 35 = 1\,225$$

$$45^2 = 45 \times 45 = 2\,025$$

$$55^2 = 55 \times 55 = 3\,025$$

Etc.

Take the tens digit, add on 1 and multiply the result with the tens digit, then stick on 25 to the end of the number.

So for 65^2, take the 6, add on 1 and multiply 6×7 and attach the 25 getting $4\,225$.

And for 95^2, take the 9, add on 1 and multiply 9×10 and attach the 25 getting 9025.

It works as far as you want to go and is pretty impressive for $995^2 = 99 \times 100 + 25 = 990025$.

CHAPTER 32

The Mean Mathematics Teacher

My pupils were not immediately impressed by the story of the mean mathematics teacher who once asked if anyone would weed his garden for one hour a day from Monday to Friday for four weeks. He was offering 1p for the first day, 2p for the second day, 4p for the third day, and so on, doubling the hourly rate every day. 'Slave labour!' they all agreed. 'We'll stick to picking strawberries.'

But once they started writing down the figures …
1 + 2 + 4 + 8 + 16 + 32 + 64 … nothing startling so far, but let's keep going … + 128 + 256 + 512 + 1 024 + 2 048 + 4 096 + 8 192 … We're only at the fourteenth day and already the hourly rate is £81.92. On the last day the pay is 524 388 or £5 243.88 with the total for the twenty days coming to an amazing £10 486.75.

Not bad for twenty hours weeding. Later they learned that the quickest way to get the total is to use the calculator and key in the formula $2^{20} - 1$.

$-\pi-$

π (pi) is the ratio obtained when the distance round the circumference C of a circle is divided by the diameter D.

Introducing π is best done by a practical method so my class and I always went outside to the quadrangle where we drew large circles on the ground using a piece of chalk attached to a length of string. We measured C and D by stepping toe to heel around and across the circle. The units of measurement we invented had names like Billyfeet, Angelafeet and even dainty, high-heeled teacherfeet.

Then we returned to the classroom and did our calculations. We all got 3 and a bit which was a better result than that obtained by King Solomon in the Bible (Kings 7:23) who thought π was exactly 3.

> And he made a molten sea, ten cubits from one
> brim to the other: it was round all about, and
> its height was five cubits: and a line of thirty
> cubits did compass it round about.

Although for school calculations, we use 3.14 for π, the decimal places for π go on for ever. One obsessed sixteenth century mathematician, Ludolf van Ceulen, spent most of his life on the calculation of π finally getting to 35 decimal places and this is engraved on his tombstone in the Dutch town of Leiden.

Another obsessive was boarding school headmaster and mathematician, William Shanks (1812–82) who spent twenty years calculating π to 707 decimal places. He calculated all

morning and spent all afternoon checking his morning's work. When the 707 decimal places were studied, the digit 7 appeared fewer times than the other digits. Since little is required to make mathematicians excited, the elusive 7 had them all buzzing and scratching their heads.

However, long after Mr Shanks's death, another mathematician found an error in the poor man's calculation. It was wrong from the 527th place and in the corrected version 7 appeared with the same frequency as every other digit.

Calculating π to as many decimal places as possible has never lost its glamour. With the considerable help of a powerful Hitachi computer, Japanese mathematician, Kanada Takahashi, has calculated over 206 billion decimal places for π. Yes, that's 206 followed by nine zeros! There is no pattern in the numbers and none of the digits from 0 to 9 appear more or less than any others. It seems that the digits are completely random. But what use is all that stuff? I am tempted to say that Kanada should find another more interesting hobby.

A parent once sent in a book whose pages were covered in figures. The book's title was π.

We didn't think it would be a bestseller.

CHAPTER 34

You Can Always Rely on Algebra

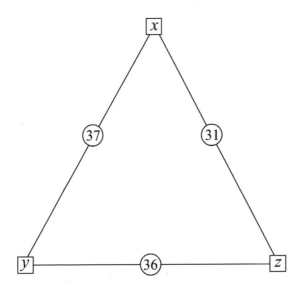

In the diagram, find the numbers, x, y, and z so that each circled number is equal to the sum of the numbers on its side.

You may be tempted to try guessing but believe me, you'll be at this page for ages. However, you can always rely on Algebra.

$$x + y = 37$$

$$x + z = 31$$

$$y + z = 36$$

Add the equations

$$2x + 2y + 2z = 104$$

So $x + y + z = 52$

But $x + y = 37$

So $z = 15$ and $y = 21$ and $x = 16$

Isn't that a neat little bit of algebra?

CHAPTER 35

The Googol

M y younger pupils often wanted to know what the very biggest number is. Well, of course, it doesn't exist. Obviously a trillion (1 000 000 000 000) can't be the largest number because a trillion + 1 is bigger.

A mathematician called Dr Edward Kasner, asked his nine-year-old nephew to think up a name for the brain boggling number 1 followed by a hundred zeros. In a few seconds, the little boy said it should be called a googol and so the enormous number was christened.

How many trillions are there in a googol? Well, the googol is 1 with 100 zeros and a trillion is 1 with 12 zeros so cancelling out the 12 zeros on the bottom line with 12 of the zeros on the top line leaves 88 zeros, so the answer is 10 to the power of 88. According to a Latin scholar friend of mine, the Latin for 88 is *octogintaocto*, so 10 to the power of 88 could be called an *octogintaoctoillion* (what do you think?) … I'm sure there's another nine-year-old who could come up with something neater.

I told my class that the number of raindrops falling in

Scotland for a whole century would probably be smaller than a googol. This statement was always followed by a stunned silence interrupted by the occasional 'Wow!'

The computer geniuses Larry Page and Sergey Brin, the founders of Google, named their research engine after the term googol. The little spelling error has not stood in the way of their success and they are now billionaires.

That's a 1 with only nine zeros.

CHAPTER 36

Infinity

Great-Aunt Marilla left all her fortune to the Peruvian Donkey Protection League and there was no money left to share between her ten hopeful nephews and nieces. In maths:

$$0 \div 10 = 0$$

Have you ever wondered about **10 ÷ 0**? Surely the answer to that is also 0?

No, it certainly is not! If you try **10 ÷ 0** on your calculator, the machine goes into nervous breakdown mode and shouts, '**ERROR!**' The calculator can't cope with it, nor can any human being!

Let's try a few divisions:

$$10 \div 10 = 1$$

$$10 \div 5 = 2$$

$$10 \div 1 = 10$$

$$10 \div \tfrac{1}{10} = 100$$

$$10 \div \tfrac{1}{1000} = 10\,000$$

So the smaller the number you divide by, the bigger the answer. If you divide by a very, very small fraction, you can get a very, very, big answer which could be much bigger even than a googol. Eventually, as the divisor gets nearer and nearer to zero, the answer will be so big that we can't enumerate it and we call it **infinity**.

So we say that:

$$\text{Any number (X)} \div 0 = \infty$$
(Like the figure 8 sideways)

There was always some little smarty-pants in the class who put his hand up. I knew what he was going to ask before he said it. 'Miss, what about $0 \div 0$?' Well, $0 \div 10 = 0$ as in Great Aunt Marilla's non-existent fortune which was to be divided between her nephews and nieces. So surely $0 \div 0 = 0$? On the other hand, $5 \div 5 = 1$, in fact any number divided by itself equals 1 so maybe $0 \div 0 = 1$. But we have just demonstrated that a number divided by 0 is infinity. We are probably barking up three wrong trees and none of these suggestions is correct. So I don't know! Does anybody know?

And to complicate matters even further, ∞ is not really a number. It is a tricky, slippery concept that ordinary mortals cannot comprehend.

CHAPTER 37

How to Prove that 2 = 1

We can use some rather suspect algebra to prove that 2 = 1. Let a and b be two numbers which are equal but not 0, that is, a = b.

If a = b

then $a^2 = ab$

and $a^2 - b^2 = ab - b^2$

factorizing,

$(a - b)(a + b) = b(a - b)$

divide both sides by $(a - b)$

so $a + b = b$

but a = b

so 2b = b

and therefore **2 = 1**

Now, there must be something wrong here but where is the error?

Give up? It's at the stage, 'Divide both sides by (a − b)'. Since on this occasion, a = b, (a − b) = 0.

From the previous page, you know that all hell breaks forth when you try to divide by 0.

CHAPTER 38

Blaise Pascal

(1623–62)

Blaise Pascal was born in Clermont-Ferrand in France. He was educated by his father and showed a remarkable aptitude for mathematics at a very early age.

His father forbade him to do any more maths until he was proficient in Latin and Greek. But one day he found his ten-year-old son writing the proof that the angles of a triangle add up to 180 degrees on the garden wall with a piece of coal. Realizing that the boy was a prodigy, he lifted the ban and in the following years the young man became influential in many branches of mathematics, but in particular the Theory of Probability.

My pupils learned about Pascal when they studied his famous triangle.

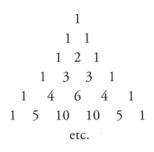

```
              1
            1   1
          1   2   1
        1   3   3   1
      1   4   6   4   1
    1   5   10   10   5   1
              etc.
```

Notice that the triangle is infinite and each row starts and ends with 1 and the number in any row is the sum of the two numbers in the row above. Also the first row starts at **1   1**. (The top single **1** merely completes the vertex of the triangle)

There is a very small chance that one of my readers might want to know that $(a + b)^3$ or any other power of $(a + b)$ can be read directly off the appropriate row of the triangle. So:

$$(a + b)^3 = 1a^3 + 3a^2b + 3ab^2 + 1b^3$$

(in practice, the '1' is always omitted).

But for ordinary mortals including most 13-year-old pupils, Pascal's Triangle has far more interesting uses. For example, in a family of four children, what is the chance that they will all be boys?

Well, look at row 4 of the triangle.

1	4	6	4	1
BBBB	BBBG	BBGG	BGGG	GGGG

$$1+4+6+4+1 = 16,$$

So there is a 1 in 16 chance of 4 boys.

A 4 in 16 chance of 3 boys and a girl.

A 6 in 16 chance of 2 boys and 2 girls.

A 4 in 16 chance of 1 boy and 3 girls.

And a 1 in 16 chance of 4 girls.

My own father was the seventh son in a family of 11 boys. The probability of having 11 boys in a family of 11 children (from the 11th row of the triangle) is **1 in 2048**.

Naturally, my pupils had to do some practical testing of the triangle. This meant an awful lot of coins being tossed and an awful lot of noise. I learned throughout the years to establish strict rules for coin tossing.

1. Paper cups and 1p coins only (larger
    denominations sometimes disappeared).

2. Anyone dropping a coin on the floor had to stop
    the test.

3. Coins had to be rattled in the cup for a maximum of two seconds.

4. The coins had to be dropped from the cup from a height not exceeding ten centimetres.

What is the probability of getting two heads when two coins are tossed together?

The theoretical results from row 2 of Pascal's Triangle are:

1	2	1
HH	HT	TT

Therefore there is 1 chance in 4 of getting 2 heads or 2 tails and 2 chances in 4 (or 1 in 2) of getting a head and a tail.

It was amazing how close the practical results were to the theoretical results. In a class of 30, each pupil was allowed 20 throws and the results were noted on the blackboard by the recorder. Youngsters loved to write on the blackboard so this was a special treat for one very delighted child.

The class always begged to continue the test with three or even four coins. If there was the possibility of a cup of black coffee and two aspirins at the end of the lesson, I usually relented.

CHAPTER 39

Magic Numbers

3367

I am willing to give up one of my favourite secret pin numbers in order to share its magic.

1. $3367 \times 69 = 232323$

2. $3367 \times 51 = 171717$

3. $3367 \times 29 = 97643$

4. $3367 \times 84 = 282828$

5. $3367 \times 47 = 158249$

6. $3367 \times 99 = 333333$

7. $3367 \times 18 = 60606$

I bet you would use a calculator. But you can do all or at least 1 2 4 6 and 7 in your head in a second.

In all of them write out the multiplier twice more and simply divide by 3.

1. $696969 \div 3 = 232323$

2. $515151 \div 3 = 171717$

3. $292929 \div 3 = 97463$

4. $848484 \div 3 = 282828$

5. $474747 \div 3 = 158249$

6. $999999 \div 3 = 333333$

7. $181818 \div 3 = 60606$

It only works for two digit multipliers and is easiest for multipliers which divide by 3.

1 2 3 4 5 6 7 8 9

'Here's another party trick for you,' I would say to my pupils. 'Multiply **123456789** by **8** and you get **987654312**. Note the neat reversal of the last two digits.'

'Mrs Strachan,' they would shake their heads sadly, 'just how many parties do you get invited to?'

CHAPTER 40

Isaac Newton

(1642–1727)

I saac Newton was a brilliant scientist and mathematician whose genius became apparent at an early age.

Unlike other boys, he was totally focused on mathematics, an activity his stepfather vehemently disapproved of. At one time the boy was so unhappy that he threatened to burn down the house with his mother and stepfather in it.

After trying unsuccessfully to be a farmer to please his mother, now widowed for a second time, Newton, with the help of his old school headmaster, got a place at Trinity College, Cambridge. Here, at last, he had a quiet haven in which to steep himself in the subjects he loved and think for long peaceful hours about how the universe worked.

In 1665–6, the Great Plague broke out in England and one fifth of the population of London died. In 1666, the Great Fire of London destroyed much of the poor housing in which the bubonic plague had flourished. During this time, Cambridge University had to close down and normal life was suspended. Newton retreated to his isolated house in Lincolnshire and took advantage of his home confinement to develop a new field of mathematics which was later called 'Calculus'.

Unknown to Newton, another mathematician in Germany, Gottfried Wilhelm Leibniz, was also working along the same lines, although using a different notation. Nowadays, both notations are used and both men are equally credited with the invention of calculus.

Calculus is now a powerful tool in the development of engineering and electronics, but for those pupils whose careers went off in a different direction, the following mysterious hieroglyphics will only be a hazy, but not unpleasant memory:

$$f'(x) = \text{Lim}(x \to 0) \; \frac{f(x + h) - f(x)}{h}$$

and

$$\int x^2 \, dx = x^3/3 + C$$

Newton's most famous work was the 500 page *Principia Mathematica*. In it are Newton's Three Laws of Motion which everyone learns at school. At the time it was double Dutch to his contemporaries. One of them was heard to say, 'There goes a man who hath writ a book no one understands.' The fact that it was written in Latin would not have helped either. In typical Newton fashion, he said he had made these astonishing mathematical discoveries by 'thinking on it continually'. And no doubt this is exactly what he had done. His concentration on his subject was intense and he had little interest in anything else.

Newton was prone to dark depressions. A lonely, introverted man, he had few friends and never married, so the popular story of his encounter with the apple comes as a little light relief.

He was taking a walk with his niece when a large apple fell from a high branch. Some killjoys insist that Newton merely observed the apple falling, but those who hate to let the truth get in the way of a good story prefer to think that the apple fell on his head with such a thud that its impact jolted him into a flash of understanding and he immediately conceived the Universal Law of Gravitation.

The apple tree also became famous. Trinity College, justifiably proud of their former student, claims the tree growing near the main gate is a direct descendant of the original source of Newton's inspiration.

Newton was also fascinated by rainbows, and anyone who studies rainbows must have at least some poetry in his soul. The great man never believed that there was a pot of gold at the end of a rainbow nor that it was a magic bridge between life and death, but he was the first to assert that rainbows have the seven colours: red, orange, yellow, green, blue, indigo and violet (mnemonic, Richard of York gave battle in vain).

Newton's other interest was alchemy, and as a diversion from his maths, he spent long, lonely hours in his laboratory doing experiments in witch-like bubbling cauldrons. He died of mercury poisoning, probably caused by an experiment that went tragically wrong. Foul play was never suspected.

CHAPTER 41

Irrational Numbers

Adam is accusing his wife of not being endowed with the power of reason. He says to her, 'Your suspicion is totally irrational, darling. Just because I was late home does not necessarily mean I was with Melissa.'

'Irrational' in maths has nothing to do with jealous wives being unreasonable. An ir**ratio**nal number is simply a number which cannot be converted to a ratio or fraction.

π and $\sqrt{2}$ are irrational numbers because their decimal places go on for ever and so cannot be expressed as fractions.

But $\sqrt{6\frac{1}{4}}$ *is* rational because it equals $2\frac{1}{2}$ exactly.

The square roots of most whole numbers are irrational except, of course, for the perfect squares, 1 4 9 16 25 36 49 64 81 100 etc. It seems very strange that the Pythagoreans hated the very thought of them.

And, by the way, the suspicious thoughts of Adam's wife were not irrational. They were perfectly rational. A neighbour spotted him in an Italian restaurant with the gorgeous Melissa.

CHAPTER 42

René Descartes

(1596–1650)

The French mathematician René Descartes started life as the frail, sickly child of a rich father. He was permitted to spend as much time as he wanted in bed where he studied mathematics and did a lot of thinking about the world.

It is said that one morning as he was lying in bed looking at the ceiling, he noticed a fly crawling over the tiles. He realized he could describe the fly's position using the intersecting lines of the tiles. These lines became the x-axis and the y-axis and where they met was called the origin. The fly is first at point (2, 2), then at point (7, –4) etc.

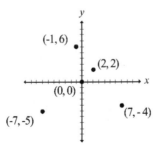

Thus began a new field of mathematics, a combination of algebra and geometry which was called Cartesian Coordinate Geometry. Straight lines and geometric shapes such as circles and parabolas all have their unique position on the coordinate plane and are all identified by their own unique algebraic equations. This sounds complicated but the Descartes system is elegantly simple and my pupils happily studied it throughout their years in school, with the 16-year-olds going on to tackle 3-dimensional coordinates.

In the diagram below, the straight line has its own name (or equation) $y = -2x + 3$.

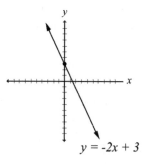

$y = -2x + 3$

The **minus** shows that the line is backward sloping, the **2** shows that on any part of the line the vertical units divided by the horizontal units (the gradient) is 2 and the **3** is where the line cuts the y-axis.

The two diagrams below illustrate a parabola and a cubic curve both of which have their own unique equation to distinguish them from an infinite number of others.

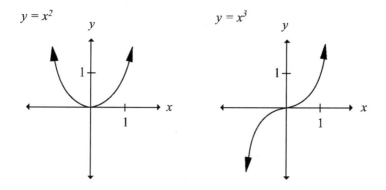

Descartes' health improved when he grew up and surprisingly, he decided to join the army. Later, he made up for lost time and went touring round Europe and spent a few years meeting friends and enjoying himself. But eventually, he settled in Holland and devoted himself to mathematics and his other great passion, philosophy.

In 1650, he was asked to take the post of tutor to young Queen Christina of Sweden. The queen insisted on having her lessons at five in the morning. The library was unheated and the castle was draughty. Descartes was too frail to withstand the extreme cold of the Swedish winter and died of pneumonia.

CHAPTER 43

Showing Off

When half my class disappeared for an orchestra rehearsal or there had been a fire drill practice and we had only 15 minutes before the bell rang, I would write this number on the blackboard in huge figures.

$$526315789473684210$$

This isn't any old number. It is the fraction $1 \div 19$ calculated until the figures start to repeat after 18 decimal places. I put the zero last instead of in its proper place at the beginning. My pupils would have been suspicious of a number which started with zero.

I then boasted that I could multiply this number in my head by anything from 2 to 18. This number is too long for an ordinary calculator so my claim had to be checked in the old fashioned way with paper and pencil and great gnashing of teeth. The class divided into working groups and tackled the smaller multipliers. Multiplying by 18 would have been too much to ask and start a rebellion.

I stood at the back of the classroom and did an Oscar-worthy performance of one whose brain is being tested to the limit. In fact, as I later revealed, the number is circular and all you need to do is find the correct starting point. Then the answer can simply be read off, adding a zero at the end. If you wish to multiply by 5, start at the digit after the first 5, or the digit after the second 5 for multiplying by 15, likewise for 2 and 12, 3 and 13 etc. For example:

$$526315789473684210 \times 16 =$$
$$8421052631578947360$$

Once or twice, I got a request from home. 'What was that number again? I wanted to show it to my dad.'

CHAPTER 44

John Napier

(1550–1617)

P iles of redundant books of log tables are only gathering dust in maths store cupboards now because in the early 1980s electronic calculators became available at ever-decreasing cost for all pupils. Until then, logarithms were essential. Pupils would first learn to calculate using tables of logarithms and antilogarithms. Later on they would groan their way through a study of the theory of logarithms.

Log tables were invented by the Scottish mathematician, John Napier, more than four centuries ago at the time of Mary, Queen of Scots. While Napier was engrossed in his mathematics, Scotland, in particular Edinburgh, was being torn apart by political and religious strife. Murder and intrigue were rife at the Palace of Holyrood and later, in 1587, Mary, Queen of Scots got her head chopped off with the reluctant approval of Queen Elizabeth I.

The son of a wealthy Scottish nobleman, Napier was born at, and later inherited Merchiston Castle which is now part of Edinburgh's second seat of learning, Napier University. At age thirteen, he went to study mathematics at St Andrews University.

John Napier also invented Napier's bones which were square rods made of ivory or bone for shortening the labour of multiplication and division. In addition, he brought the decimal point into common use. Until then, decimals looked as if they had been caught in a blizzard. For example, 2.4537 was written $2\ 4^{/}\ 5^{//}\ 3^{///}\ 7^{////}$.

His work with logarithms made calculation much easier and quicker. Using his log tables, a nasty multiplication or division can be replaced by simple addition and subtraction and roots and powers reduced to a mere multiplication or division by 2 or 3. This stroke of sheer genius became instantly popular with scientists and astronomers and opened the way for further advanced study.

Napier's personal life appears to be less laudable. Although he was a devoutly religious Protestant, it was rumoured that he dabbled in the black arts. He was often seen wandering around outside in his nightshirt and cap muttering to himself – though surely that was excusable for a man who was about to deliver one of the most important developments in mathematics of all time. However, it was known that he never travelled without his black spider, which he kept in an ivory box, and he also kept a black rooster which terrified his household staff.

If he thought that any of his servants had been stealing from him, he locked the suspects in a room with the rooster, one at a time, telling them to stroke the bird after which it would announce who the thief was. The wily Napier brushed charcoal into the bird's feathers, so that the innocent servants had no problem with stroking the rooster, but the guilty one only pretended to touch the bird and therefore had clean hands.

Napier had twelve children, two with his first wife who died young and ten by his second wife. It's difficult not to think of him as an austere humourless parent. He was certainly not friendly towards his neighbours. Once, when the pigeons belonging to a farmer in a nearby property were eating his grain, Napier threatened to keep any found on his fields. He was often seen filling a sack with surprisingly inert pigeons. The clever mathematician had sown peas soaked in brandy, which the pigeons had enjoyed so much they were too inebriated to fly.

John Napier died of gout – probably caused by eating too many pigeon pies with that rich brandy gravy.

CHAPTER 45

Magic Squares

My younger pupils enjoyed making up their own magic squares where the rows, columns and diagonals add up to the same number.

For the 3 × 3 magic square, they used the formula:

N + 3	N – 4	N + 1
N – 2	N	N + 2
N – 1	N + 4	N - 3

Taking N to be any number greater than 4, an infinite number of magic squares may be drawn. In the following magic square N = 10 and the sum of the rows, columns and diagonals is 30:

13	6	11
8	10	12
9	14	7

The easiest way to produce a 4 × 4 magic square is to write any 16 consecutive numbers in the grid:

6	7	8	9
10	11	12	13
14	15	16	17
18	19	20	21

Now draw another grid and:

1. switch the corner numbers;

2. switch the four centre numbers diagonally; and

3. put back the other numbers in their original places.

21	7	8	18
10	16	15	13
14	12	11	17
9	19	20	6

This time, the rows, columns and diagonals add up to 54.

The earliest magic square was recorded around 2,800 BC in China and mathematicians have been having fun with them ever since, with the squares getting bigger and bigger. As usual, there is always someone who wants to go one step further, inventing magic cubes with rows, columns, pillars and space diagonals and explaining them with complicated formulae which only the exclusive brotherhood of super brilliant mathematicians can understand.

CHAPTER 46

Pure Magic

On a previous page, I introduced my show off number 526315789473684210, which was concocted from the fraction $\frac{1}{19}$ when calculated to 18 decimal places, with the zero at the end instead of the beginning. (After that, the 18 digits repeat for ever.)

Arrange the calculations for $\frac{2}{19}, \frac{3}{19} \ldots \frac{18}{19}$ in a table.

$\frac{1}{19}$	0	5	2	6	3	1	5	7	8	9	4	7	3	6	8	4	2	1
$\frac{2}{19}$	1	0	5	2	6	3	1	5	7	8	9	4	7	3	6	8	4	2
$\frac{3}{19}$	1	5	7	8	9	4	7	3	6	8	4	2	1	0	5	2	6	3
$\frac{4}{19}$	2	1	0	5	2	6	3	1	5	7	8	9	4	7	3	6	8	4
$\frac{5}{19}$	2	6	3	1	5	7	8	9	4	7	3	6	8	4	2	1	0	5
$\frac{6}{19}$	3	1	5	7	8	9	4	7	3	6	8	4	2	1	0	5	2	6
$\frac{7}{19}$	3	6	8	4	2	1	0	5	2	6	3	1	5	7	8	9	4	7
$\frac{8}{19}$	4	2	1	0	5	2	6	3	1	5	7	8	9	4	7	3	6	8
$\frac{9}{19}$	4	7	3	6	8	4	2	1	0	5	2	6	3	1	5	7	8	9
$\frac{10}{19}$	5	2	6	3	1	5	7	8	9	4	7	3	6	8	4	2	1	0
$\frac{11}{19}$	5	7	8	9	4	7	3	6	8	4	2	1	0	5	2	6	3	1
$\frac{12}{19}$	6	3	1	5	7	8	9	4	7	3	6	8	4	2	1	0	5	2
$\frac{13}{19}$	6	8	4	2	1	0	5	2	6	3	1	5	7	8	9	4	7	3
$\frac{14}{19}$	7	3	6	8	4	2	1	0	5	2	6	3	1	5	7	8	9	4
$\frac{15}{19}$	7	8	9	4	7	3	6	8	4	2	1	0	5	2	6	3	1	5
$\frac{16}{19}$	8	4	2	1	0	5	2	6	3	1	5	7	8	9	4	7	3	6
$\frac{17}{19}$	8	9	4	7	3	6	8	4	2	1	0	5	2	6	3	1	5	7
$\frac{18}{19}$	9	4	7	3	6	8	4	2	1	0	5	2	6	3	1	5	7	8

If you discount the fractions column, this is an 18 × 18 pure magic square with every row, every column and both diagonals adding up to **81**.

CHAPTER 47

Fibonacci

(1170–1250)

Fibonacci, also known as Leonardo of Pisa, was one of the most talented mathematicians of the Middle Ages. He wrote, by hand, a huge work, *Liber Abaci* (*The Book of Calculation*) which has survived the intervening 800 years and whose English translation amounts to 672 pages.

When my 13-year-old pupils studied number patterns, they found one of the most interesting to be the Fibonacci Sequence. 'Feeee-bon-a-chee,' they all chorused in their best Italian accents.

I hope when they read *The Da Vinci Code* by Dan Brown or watched the film, they still remembered the sequence. The dying curate attempted to pass on, in code, the secret he did not want to take to the grave. It was fortunate that Langdon and Sophie Neveu recognized the Fibonacci Sequence whose pattern starts as follows:

1 1 2 3 5 8 13 21 34 55 89 144 …

Each number is the sum of the two before. This is an amazing set of numbers which has many applications, especially in nature.

To make the lesson more interesting, we spent ten minutes in the nearby park and picked some daisies. (Children are delighted to leave the classroom for any reason, even a dental appointment to have teeth extracted.) We tore off the petals and counted them. During the next few weeks, they brought in flowers from their own gardens and we collected the following information.

Name of flower	Number of Petals
Lily	3
Buttercup, pansy	5
Delphinium	8
Marigold, osteo spernum	13
Aster	21
Pyrethrum	34
Daisy	34 or 55

Is it a coincidence that they are all Fibonacci numbers? We didn't think so.

I once tried to interest the class in the puzzle about the Fibonacci rabbits which goes like this:

A man puts a pair of baby rabbits into a large enclosed garden. They cannot breed until they are two months old but at the end of the third month, they produce a new pair of rabbits which in turn become productive at two months old. If nature takes its course and they are all producing in the notorious way that rabbits do, how many rabbits will there be at the end of the year. To solve this problem, look no further than the Fibonacci sequence.

End of month	1	2	3	4	5	6	7	8	9	10	11	12
No. of pairs	1	1	2	3	5	8	13	21	34	55	89	144

My class were not happy about this problem. 'What if some of them die or tunnel under the fence?' 'What if there are more boy bunnies born than girl bunnies?' 'What if some of the boy rabbits are gay?'

The self appointed expert on rabbits put his hand up. 'Please Miss,' he said, 'my cousin has two rabbits called Thumper and Cuddles. They had a litter of eight babies. My uncle drowned them all and Thumper had to go to the vet to have an operation on his willy.'

I moved on quickly to the next part of the lesson before the protestations about mass rabbit genocide and the violation of Thumper's rabbit rights to procreate got out of hand.

Fibonacci's rabbits have been in the garden again!

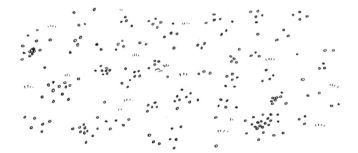

CHAPTER 48

Fibonacci Meets Pythagoras

The Fibonacci Sequence is 1 1 2 3 5 8 13 21 34 55 89 144 … Take any four numbers along the line (but not too far along the line if you don't have a calculator at hand). For example:

2 3 5 8. Multiply the outside numbers, 2 × 8 = 16

Multiply the inside numbers and double,
3 × 5 = 15 × 2 = 30.

16 and 30 are the legs of a right-angled triangle.

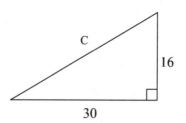

Using the Theorem of Pythagoras, we can calculate the hypotenuse:

$$C^2 = 16^2 + 30^2$$
$$= 256 + 900$$
$$= 1156$$
$$C = \sqrt{1156} = 34$$

Notice that 34 is also a Fibonacci number further along the line.

The area of the above triangle is $\frac{1}{2} \times 30 \times 16 = 240$ square units. If you take the chosen block of numbers 2 3 5 8 and multiply them, you get 240.

This works (as far as I know) all along the line but with all that squaring and adding the calculation gets quite tedious without a calculator.

Fibonacci meets Pythagoras! Who could deny that maths is magic?

CHAPTER 49

Who is the Fairest of Us All?

This is another quickie when there are five minutes to fill in.

1. Choose a number between 1 and 9.

2. Multiply it by 3.

3. Add 3

4. Multiply by 3 again.

5. Add the digits of your answer together.

Now who is the most gorgeous person in the class? Is it:

1. Chris

2. Angela

3. David

4. Ashleigh

5. Jack

6. Maggie

7. Ellie

8. Rowen

9. You!

10. Lauren

Of course it's you!

This is based on simple algebra:

1. x

2. 3x

3. 3x + 3

4. 9x + 9.

Whatever number you choose for x, 9x + 9 will be a number on the nine times table and the digits of these numbers always add to 9.

CHAPTER 50

Getting the Time Right

The Julian calendar, introduced in 46 BC, was used in most civilized countries. Mathematicians had calculated that the year – the time the earth takes to do its circuit round the sun – was 365¼ days, or 365 days 6 hours.

Much later, mathematicians calculated that the length of the year was in fact only 365.2422 days. Take the decimal part 0.2422 and multiply by 24 getting 5.8128 hours. Take the decimal part again, 0.8128 and multiply by 60 getting 48.768 minutes and once again multiply the decimal part 0.768 by 60 getting 46.08 seconds. So the more accurate calculation for the length of the year is 365 days, 5 hours, 48 minutes and 46.08 seconds.

In 325 AD, the Julian calendar was established in every Christian country. Unfortunately it was wrong by eleven minutes every year so, in 1592, the Vatican ordered that the new, more accurate Gregorian calendar should be adopted throughout Roman Catholic Europe. At that time, Queen Elizabeth I was on the throne of England. Her father, King Henry VIII, had fallen out with the pope over his marriage to

Elizabeth's mother, Anne Boleyn. The Church of England was now firmly established and Elizabeth wanted nothing to do with any popish calendar.

However, by 1752, in the reign of George II, Britain had fallen behind by eleven days. So to catch up, the day after September 2nd was followed by September 14th.

This was very confusing to the general population. Just imagine it. Many had no birthday that year, appointments vanished into thin air, workmen complained that they had lost eleven days' wages. There was probably an announcement in the *London Society News*, 'Lord and Lady Fotheringale-Smythe are pleased to announce the birth of their twin sons. William was born at five minutes before midnight on September 2nd and James arrived at three minutes past midnight on September 14th.'

Everyone thought their lives had been shortened by eleven days. Protesters marched in the streets shouting, 'Give us back our eleven days!'

Mathematicians say the Gregorian calendar is still ever so slightly inaccurate and in 3,000 years' time, it will have to be adjusted by one day.

But let's not bother ourselves about that.

CHAPTER 51

Monday's Child is Fair of Face

I t is surprising how few children know on which day of the week they were born and they are always keen to find out.

Every teacher knows that on the last few days before the summer holidays, all lessons have to be heavily disguised. This is when I wrote the famous old nursery rhyme on the blackboard.

Monday's child is fair of face.

Tuesday's child is full of grace.

Wednesday's child is full of song.

Thursday's child is brave and strong.

Friday's child is loving and giving.

Saturday's child works hard for a living.

But the child who is born on the Seventh day,

Has great success along life's highway.

OK! I have changed the original version just a bit. I really had to. What Wednesday's child wants to be full of woe? And as for Sunday's child being good and gay, heaven forbid!

First of all, I had to explain the meaning of 'grace'. The Chambers Dictionary says 'grace' is easy elegance in form or manner; any unassumingly attractive or pleasing personal quality. Even my bored uninterested girls who possessed none of these attributes perked up and looked delighted at the idea of being a Tuesday's child. I also assured any potential Saturday's children that although they would be working hard, it would be at a very important and very well paid job. I then sneaked in the maths.

The calculation of the day is quite easy although there is a little complication which I will explain later.

The calendar says that Christmas Day 2009 will be a Friday. Let's see if we can prove it.

First we write the date under four headings:

1. Y_1 is the first two digits of the year (20)

2. Y_2 is the second two digits of the year (09)

3. M is the month, in this example December (12)

4. D is the day (25)

First Step

Divide Y_1 by 4 (if necessary, ignore any
remainder) $20 \div 4 = 5$
Subtract twice Y_1 $5 - 40 = -35$
Subtract 1 $-35 - 1 = \underline{-36}$

Second Step

Multiply Y_2 by 5 and divide by 4
(ignore any remainder) $9 \times 5 \div 4 = \underline{11}$

Third Step

Add 1 to M, multiply by 26 and then divide by
10 (again ignoring any remainder)
$(12 + 1) \times 26 \div 10 = \underline{33}$

Fourth Step

Write down the day $\underline{25}$
Now add the underlined numbers in the four
steps: $-36 + 11 + 33 + 25 = \underline{33}$

Fifth Step

Divide 33 by 7 but this time ignore the answer
and take note of the remainder.
$33 \div 7 = 4$ R 5. The remainder is $\underline{5}$

Number	Day
0	Sunday
1	Monday
2	Tuesday
3	Wednesday
4	Thursday
5	Friday
6	Saturday

Yes, Christmas Day 2009 is a Friday.

The little complication

If the months you choose are January or February, consider these as months 13 and 14 of the previous year. For example,

1. 26 January 1960. Y_1 = 19, but Y_2 = 59. M = 13 and D = 26

2. 21 February 2012. Y_1 = 20 but Y_2 = 11. M = 14 and D = 21.

That filled in the last maths lesson of the session very nicely and all the class went home for the summer holidays very happy that their wonderful personalities had been confirmed by mathematical calculation.

CHAPTER 52

Dopey Donald Gets Lucky

I t's probably not good teaching practice to show a class how *not* to do something. But I sometimes did, as in the following story.

A teacher wrote three fractions on the blackboard and asked the class to cancel them down to their simplest form.

1. $\frac{16}{64}$

2. $\frac{19}{95}$

3. $\frac{26}{65}$

Brainy Brian did everything he had been taught.

1. $\frac{16}{64} = \frac{1}{4}$ The teacher's pet divided the numerator and the denominator, or in simple language, the top and bottom lines by 8 and then by 2.

2. $^{19}\!/_{95} = \frac{1}{5}$ Brainy Brian knew that $95 \div 19 = 5$.

3. $^{26}\!/_{65} = \frac{2}{5}$ Brian even knew his 13 times table.

This is what Dopey Donald did.

1. $^{16}\!/_{64}$ He crossed out the 6s and was left with the correct answer of $\frac{1}{4}$.

2. $^{19}\!/_{95}$ He did the same with the 9s and got the correct answer of $\frac{1}{5}$.

3. $^{26}\!/_{65}$ Again, he crossed out the 6s and got $\frac{2}{5}$, which is correct.

Dopey Donald was convinced he had discovered a new method for cancelling fractions. But it only works for the above fractions. It does *not* work for $^{18}\!/_{81}$, $^{21}\!/_{42}$ or $^{15}\!/_{55}$ and millions and millions of other fractions. So do *not* copy Dopey Donald's crazy cancelling.

CHAPTER 53

Vulgar and Improper Fractions

VULGAR FRACTIONS

Fractions are either decimal or common, 0.5 or ½. Common fractions are often called vulgar fractions. Now everyone knows that 'vulgar' means rude and disgusting, which is what the 12-year-old girls think of Peter who is a serial nose picker.

But 'vulgar' comes from the Latin word *vulgus* who were the common people of Rome, so vulgar fractions are simply the fractions that the ordinary man in the street uses. He asks for half a pint of beer and when Mum cuts up the homemade apple pie for her husband and three children, they don't get a 0.2 share. Everybody gets a fifth.

Meanwhile, a top heavy fraction like ³⁄₂ or ⁷⁄₃ is often called an improper fraction.

'Improper' means inappropriate or lacking in modesty or decency so this is really a very silly name to call top heavy fractions. I preferred not to use it.

CHAPTER 54

Pythagoras and Adding Fractions

T ake any two consecutive odd numbers or any two consecutive even numbers. For example, 5 and 7. Write
down their reciprocals and add them. (The reciprocal of any
number x is the fraction you get when you divide 1 by x.)

$$\tfrac{1}{5} + \tfrac{1}{7} = \tfrac{12}{35}$$

OK, I know! You don't see where the 12 and 35 come from?
For those who have long since forgotten how to add or subtract
the dreaded fractions, here is a sure-fire method.

Take the larger denominator and say its times table until
the smaller one divides in. So we have 7, 14, 21, 28, 35. Stop
there because 5 goes into 35.

So $\tfrac{1}{5} = \tfrac{7}{35}$ and $\tfrac{1}{7} = \tfrac{5}{35}$ giving $\tfrac{12}{35}$.

Let's resume:

Now taking the 12 and 35 as the legs of a right-angled triangle, calculate the hypotenuse

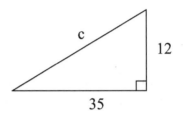

$$c^2 = a^2 + b^2$$

$$= 12^2 + 35^2$$

$$= 144 + 1225$$

$$= 1369$$

$$c = \sqrt{1369} = 37$$

giving the Pythagorean triple (12, 35, 37)

This works for any pair of odd or even consecutive numbers and was particularly useful when I needed an unfamiliar set of Pythagorean triples for examination purposes.

CHAPTER 55

Charles Babbage

(1791–1871)

Most of the famous mathematicians we remember were able to do their work without pressure and without worrying about money. Some were wealthy men in their own right, others were recognized as being extraordinarily gifted, like Gauss, and given every encouragement and support.

Charles Babbage was also wealthy and was equally gifted, but he ended up a broken man, his genius unappreciated.

Life started off well. As the son of a very rich banker, he had the best education London could offer. He became a brilliant mathematician and mechanical engineer and his skills in those fields led him to invent the first mechanical computer.

The first machine was called the Difference Engine. Politicians of the day were impressed with the model and granted a large sum of money for its construction. The finished machine was to weigh 15 tons, stand 8 feet high, have about 25,000 parts, and would perform calculations to at least 16 significant figures. An engineer named Joseph Clement was appointed to build it but soon problems arose. There was personal conflict between the two men, the project was going to cost much more than was expected and Babbage refused to hand over more of his own money. Clement and his team of workers would not proceed without further funding. They stopped the construction and it was never resumed.

Meanwhile, Babbage had started on a second model capable of carrying out even more advanced mathematical operations than the first Difference Engine but the government refused any further money because the first machine had not been completed.

Babbage was becoming a laughing stock. During one of his many unsuccessful visits to the House of Commons to seek funding for his second machine, a member jokingly asked the following question, 'Pray, Mr Babbage, if you put wrong figures into the machine, would the right figures come out?'

Babbage's sharp reply was the nineteenth-century version of the well known acronym in modern computer science, GIGO or 'garbage in, garbage out' and his tormentor was silenced.

Understandably, Babbage became embittered and angry and it is tragic that this gifted mathematician, so ahead of his time, was treated in this way. However, he was not a charismatic man. In modern day parlance, his interpersonal communication skills needed serious upgrading and anecdotes show him to be a rather humourless Victorian fuddy-duddy.

He certainly was a stickler for accuracy. Having read the poem, 'The Vision of Sin' by Alfred, Lord Tennyson, he felt compelled to write and complain about the following lines:

Every moment dies a man.

Every moment, one is born.

If this were true, Babbage pointed out, the world would be at a standstill. At that time Babbage knew that the ratio of births to deaths was 1.0625 to 1 and the mathematician suggested that the poet should amend his poem accordingly.

Sadly, Babbage never regained the respect he deserved. When he died in 1871, there was only one carriage at his funeral. *The Times* newspaper ridiculed him and the Royal Society did not publish an obituary.

However, in 1991, British scientists constructed the Difference Engine 2 from Babbage's detailed model. The machine, now in the second floor of the London Science Museum, worked perfectly and in 2002 the 4,000 part printing mechanism was added, finally completing Babbage's original vision and proving that he was worthy of joining the mathematicians' roll of honour.

CHAPTER 56

Triskaidekaphobia

(fear of the number 13)

BE VERY AFRAID
OF NUMBER
THIRTEEN!

One morning in my classroom, a heavy blind suddenly detached itself from the window and fell on the floor with a loud clatter. Our janitor who came to tidy up the mess, reminded us that it was Friday the Thirteenth.

Nasty things happen on that day so many people won't drive a car, some even refuse to go to work and couples never choose that day to get married.

This superstition has many supposed origins. In the Middle Ages, Friday was 'hanging day' for criminals and there were 13 steps up to the gallows. My bloodthirsty pupils always like this idea.

The number 13 itself is notoriously unlucky. It was the number of men who sat round the table at the Last Supper, but that hardly explains why, even to this day, 13 is so feared. There is no Gate 13 at most airports, cities in the USA avoid having a 13th Street, the lifts in high buildings go from floor 12 to floor 14, and the Italian National Lottery omits the number.

Personally, I am not triskaidekaphobic. My elder son was born on Friday 13th so that was a very lucky day for me.

CHAPTER 57

The Pentagram

This five-pointed star is called a pentagram and is an amazing mathematical figure. It is connected with magic and the black arts but it is also a holy symbol in many religions. The weird Pythagoreans considered the pentagram to be mathematical perfection and they used it as their symbol of health.

In Dan Brown's book *The Da Vinci Code* the dying curate, Jacques Saunière, paints a pentagram on his chest with his own blood to give Robert Langdon a deeply significant message.

My pupils found the pentagram easy to draw with a pair of compasses, a protractor to measure angles of 72° (360° ÷ 5), and a ruler. Inside the pentagram is a perfect pentagon and if you join up the points of the star, you get another pentagon.

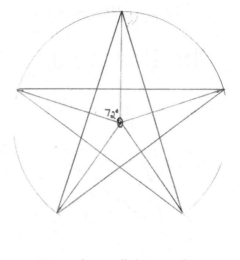

Now rub out all the extra lines

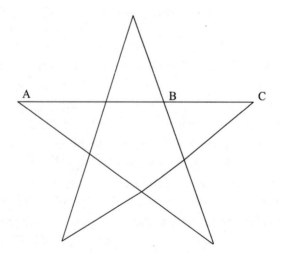

Measure the length of AC and AB as accurately as you can in millimetres and divide AC by AB. In the pentagon shown, that is 65 ÷ 40 giving 1.62 to 2 decimal places. Now do the same with AB (39) and BC (24) and this is also 1.62 to 2 decimal places.

So what? It's not high up on the scale of interesting facts, is it? Well, yes it is and the Pythagoreans were perhaps not completely bonkers after all.

Go back to the Fibonacci series, the one about the pro-creating rabbits. The series goes:

> 1 1 2 3 5 8 13 21 34 55 89 144
> 233 377 610 987 1597 2584 4181
> 6765 … with the 39th and 40th numbers
> being **63245986** and **102334155** and
> remember these numbers go on and on
> getting bigger and bigger.

Now go along the line taking any number and dividing it by the one before. As early as 21 ÷13 you get 1.62 to 2 decimal places. As you go along the line to bigger numbers, the answers start to level off. 6765 ÷ 4181 = 1.618033988749894 … and so is 102334155 ÷ 63245986.

What we have got is another of these irrational numbers which, like π, goes on for ever.

This special irrational number is called the Golden Ratio or the Divine Proportion and has its own symbol Φ or phi which is the 21st letter of the Greek alphabet.

The golden ratio is important in art, sculpture and architecture in order to get a proportion which is pleasing to the eye. It is said that the most beautiful rectangle is one with its length and breadth in the ratio of phi.

So the Pythagoreans were right. The pentagram, with all its parts conforming to the phi ratio, is truly a perfect figure.

But even before the Pythagoreans, the Egyptians who built the great Pyramid of Giza around 2500 BC seemed to know about the Golden Ratio. Or is it just a very strange coincidence that on the highest building of the ancient world, the ratio of the slant height of a triangular face to half the base is 1.618?

The Golden Ratio also appears in modern everyday life. Take out your credit card, your library card or your store card and measure its length and breadth and divide to calculate the ratio.

And guess what you will find!

CHAPTER 58

Statistics

My younger pupils loved the branch of mathematics called statistics. Of course they were sometimes allowed to escape from the classroom to collect the data but they also enjoyed drawing colourful bar graphs and pie charts and pinning them up on the wall.

I learned not to research personal things like size of family, which caused many problems. 'My mum's boyfriend sometimes has a sleepover, do I include him?' 'What about my dog, is he one of the family?' 'Do I count myself?'

So we researched innocuous subjects like eye colour, breakfast cereals, favourite potato crisp flavours, pop groups, popularity of school subjects, and makes of car in the High Street.

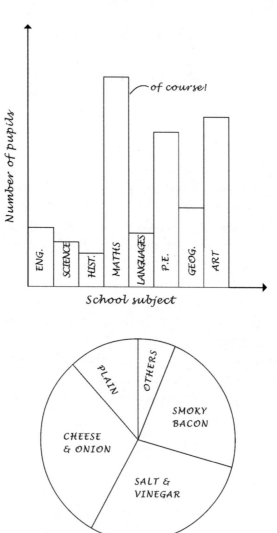

We also had fun calculating average height. First I measured them all in centimetres, girls and boys separately and recorded the data on the blackboard. They added the heights and divided by the number of pupils to get the **mean.** Then I showed them how much quicker it was to line them all up from shortest to tallest and pick out the one in the middle, the **median,** often a better measure of average as it is not distorted by abnormal data at the extremes. I emphasized this by fabricating data from the local Registrar's office.

Age of Brides Recorded During June
22 25 19 35 27 19 22 24 24 **79** 23 22 20 27 18
24 21 27 **57** 25

Adding up these ages and dividing by 20 gives a **mean** average of **28.** This is high because of the elderly bride who was reunited with her childhood sweetheart when they met again in Sunset House, and the second marriage of the 57-year-old lady. The **79** and the **57** have skewed the average. Also there is not a 28-year-old bride in the list.

Rearranging the data in ascending order gives a middle or **median** average of 24 which is more satisfactory:

18 19 19 20 21 22 22 22 23 <u>24</u> / <u>24</u> 24 25 25
27 27 27 35 57 79

Another measure of average is the **mode** which could be used for calculating, for example, average shoe size for women. There is no point in working out the **mean**. The answer would probably be a ridiculous result like 6.24. The **median** might also be misleading. It is far better to use the **mode**, the one that occurs most often. So in a shoe shop, size 6 (US 39) might be the size most asked for. Or the average might be **bimodal** with size 5 (US 38) and size 6 flying off the shelves first, and sizes 3 (US 36) and 8 (US 41) left for the January sales.

Let's go back to averages again. Suppose we need to find the mean average temperature in Santa Ponza during the month of September. The daily temperatures, in degrees Centigrade, are:

29 28 29 30 29 31 31 29 30 31 31 29 28
28 30 31 32 31 30 30 29 29 28 29 29 30
31 31 34 33

Now, some people love to add up a column of figures, others prefer to use a calculator, but either way I personally get distracted and forget where I am halfway through. So I look for easy ways. I notice that the smallest entry is 28, so I write out the data again subtracting 28, giving us:

1 0 1 2 1 3 3 1 2 3 3 1 0 0 2 3 4 3 2 2 1 1
0 1 1 2 3 3 6 5

These figures are easy to add up. The total is 60 so divide by 30 to get a mean of 2, but don't forget to add on the 28 you subtracted in the first place giving an average temperature in Santa Ponza of 30°C or 86°F (divide by 5, multiply by 9 and add 32).

CHAPTER 59

Florence Nightingale

(1820–1910)

'Florence Nightingale?' my pupils would say. 'She was the Lady with the Lamp. We learned all about her in Primary School.'

Never being one to stick to the subject, I would tell my pupils what little I knew about the Crimean War with its enormous casualty rate, especially at the Battle of Balaclava where the Light Brigade charged to their deaths for little military advantage.

'And,' I asked them, 'did you know that the cardigans you're wearing were named after the commander of the Light Brigade, Lord Cardigan, who added a woollen knitted jacket with buttons to the soldiers' uniform to combat the cold of the Crimean winter? And that's where the name of the woolly hat, the balaclava helmet comes from.' But I had lost them. They had never heard of balaclava helmets. I told them that when I was a little girl during the Second World War, I often got earache and my mother forced me to wear a multi-striped balaclava knitted by my granny from all the odd bits of wool in her knitting bag. The class, who wore headgear with fashionable sports logos, looked at me with genuine pity.

Anyway, what has Florence Nightingale got to do with maths? Well, unlike other young ladies of her generation who would barely learn enough of the subject to count their large Victorian families, Florence persuaded her father to provide her with a maths tutor, and later he relented and allowed her to train as a nurse. In the early 1840s, respectable young ladies got married; they certainly did not learn arithmetic, algebra and geometry, nor did they belittle themselves with nursing and, in particular, nursing men.

The Crimean War had been raging for two years when Florence arrived with her team of nurses at the British Army Hospital in Scutari. She was horrified at the disgusting, unsanitary conditions in the wards and set about changing things but she needed vast quantities of medical supplies and massive support.

However, she did not go immediately to the military brass hats weeping copious hysterical tears about the plight of the wounded. She knew they would despise a feminine approach and would not want their authority challenged by a woman. So she started to keep records and soon she was able to overwhelm them with statistics, indisputable facts and figures to demonstrate and drive home the seriousness of the situation. She presented her case coldly and scientifically in exactly the right way to impress the military hierarchy and the British government. Florence gave them accurate data of casualties, presented in numerical tables and statistical diagrams. Her favourite was the colourful polar-area diagram which is similar to the pie chart. The polar-area diagram is often called the Nightingale rose chart.

In February 1855, the mortality rate at Scutari was 42.7 per cent, accurately calculated by Florence, but once her hospital reforms took effect, there was a dramatic improvement and she gained the undying respect of the soldiers. When all the other medical officers had retired for the night, the Lady with the Lamp did a last round in the darkened wards, checking her most seriously wounded patients before returning to her statistics to send back to England.

After the war, she was the first woman to become a Fellow of the Royal Statistical Society and later, she was given an honorary membership of the American Statistical Association.

Although bed-ridden for many years at the end of her long life, she continued working to establish nursing as a respectable profession for women.

CHAPTER 60

The Camel Conundrum

A rich Arab was dying and he said to his sons, 'Abdul, my eldest son, I am giving you half of my camels. Bashir, my second son, you may have one third of my camels, and to you, Dilbar, I shall give one ninth of my camels.'

However, there were 17 camels and 17 doesn't divide by 2, 3 or 9. They consulted their uncle who said, 'I will lend you one of my own camels so that will make 18. Abdul will have $\frac{1}{2}$ of 18, Bashir will have $\frac{1}{3}$ of 18 and Dilbar will have $\frac{1}{9}$ of 18 making $9 + 6 + 2 = 17$ camels. Now you can return the camel I lent you.'

Although the sons were happy, there is something not quite right here.

First of all, $\frac{1}{2}$, $\frac{1}{3}$ and $\frac{1}{9}$ add to only $\frac{17}{18}$ so did the father intend to give a $\frac{1}{18}$ share to someone else?

However, they didn't have to borrow one of their uncle's camels. The boys could have worked with the fractions so, strictly speaking, Abdul should have got exactly $\frac{1}{2}$ of 17 camels which is $8\frac{1}{2}$ camels, and Bashir and Dilbar $5\frac{2}{3}$ and $1\frac{8}{9}$ camels respectively. These fractions add to $16\frac{1}{18}$. However, common sense prevailed and the shares were rounded up to 9, 6 and 2 camels to everyone's satisfaction.

Let's hope that the prodigal son called Chengiz did not turn up to claim his $^{17}/_{18}$ of a camel.

CHAPTER 61

The Knight's Tour

Once mathematicians get their teeth into a little problem, they often work and work at it until it has been solved or has defeated them. Knight's Tours have been studied by thousands of mathematicians over several centuries. I tried googling 'Knight's Tours' and in 0.26 seconds, up popped a possible 4 760 000 entries. I hastily shut it down again!

So what are Knight's Tours? The knight on a chess board moves in an 'L' shape, jumping over two squares in one direction and one square in the other. In an 8 × 8 board or any other size of square grid, the task is to discover how many ways it is possible for the knight to start on any square and visit all the other squares, once and once only.

And that's what all these mathematicians have been doing over the centuries. They've been trying to work out formulae for odd- and even-numbered squares. Some have even moved on to rectangular grids and, God forbid, 3-dimensional grids.

I showed my pupils that on a 3 × 3 grid, you get a pretty pattern but it is not a proper Knight's Tour because it is impossible to reach the centre square.

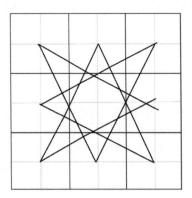

Larger grids got them tied in knots. Mathematicians have endless patience. Thirteen-year-olds do not. However, if there was an interrupted lesson, for example, when all the class were called away for their dreaded vaccinations and returned feeling sorry for themselves and nursing a tender arm, I issued an 8 × 8 grid as below. They were allowed to be six-year-olds again and all they had to do was join up the dots to produce a perfect Knight's Tour.

The poor wounded souls were quite happy to create a piece of abstract art which, of course, was displayed on the wall.

18	59	50	1	48	15	22	63
51	2	17	60	21	64	47	14
58	19	4	49	16	23	62	45
3	52	57	20	61	46	13	24
34	5	40	53	36	25	44	11
39	56	35	8	41	12	29	26
6	33	54	37	28	31	10	43
55	38	7	32	9	42	27	30

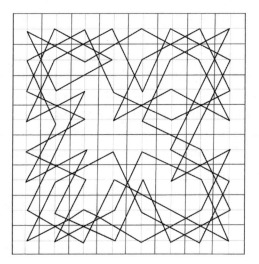

CHAPTER 62

John von Neumann

(1903–57)

J ohn von Neumann was born in Budapest. When his classmates were learning the two times table, young John could do multi-digit long divisions in his head. By the time he was twelve, he had mastered university level calculus.

In 1930, he was appointed to the prestigious post of Professor of Mathematics and Physics at Princeton University, New Jersey. His work was used in the development of atomic energy. He built one of the first electronic brains and, showing that he had a good sense of humour, he called it MANIAC (Mathematical Analyzer Numerical Integrator and Computer).

As a diversion from such mind boggling work, von Neumann liked to solve puzzles. There is more than one version of the following puzzle, which may even be an urban myth, but it is worth retelling.

> Two trains are 20 miles apart on a single track
> heading towards each other at 10 mph. At the
> same time, a bee flies off at 20 mph from the

front of one train and heads for the other train. It touches the second train, does a flip turn and flies back towards the first train and turns again. The mad bee, who should have been in the garden pollinating with his pals, continues back and forth until it is tragically crushed to death between the colliding trains. The question is, how far does the bee fly altogether?

Mathematicians may be tempted to dive into the problem by considering each leg of the bee's flight in turn, seeing a finite series pattern, forming an equation and finally coming up with the answer, 20 miles.

But schoolchildren can solve the problem by a much simpler method. The trains are travelling at 10 mph so in one hour, both having travelled 10 miles, are now touching each other with the bee squashed between them. The bee had been flying at 20 mph so in the one hour the bee has travelled **20 miles** and all its to-ings and fro-ings are irrelevant.

Of course the brilliant von Neumann came up with the correct answer in seconds, and he may have used the second method.

Ah ha! But how did he also know which train the bee was **facing** at the moment of collision?

CHAPTER 63

The Disappearing Teacher

I always encouraged the kids to ask if they didn't understand. This they did quite often ... not because there was something they didn't understand, but because the little brats loved to laugh at me saying, in all innocence, 'OK, all of you, look at the blackboard and I'll run through it once again.'

CHAPTER 64

Scientific Notation

Mathematicians and scientists often have to work with very large or very small numbers. For example, the approximate speed of light, 300 000 000 metres per second or the mass of a tiny particle, 0.0000014 grams.

Typing the correct number of zeros would make their secretaries quite cross-eyed so mathematicians invented scientific notation, a method of expressing these awkward numbers in a more concise form which avoids writing strings of zeros.

Each number is written in the form $a \times 10^n$ where a is a number between 1 and 10 and n is a positive or negative whole number. For example:

1. 186 000 000. Take the '186' bit, and insert a decimal point between the 1 and 8 to make 1.86, then count the leaps from the point to the end. In this case, there are 8 leaps so $186\,000\,000 = 1.86 \times 10^8$

2. 50 000. This time the number between 1 and 10

is 5.0 and there are 4 leaps to the end so $50\,000 = 5.0 \times 10^4$

3. 1 googol = 1.0×10^{100}

For very small numbers, you do much the same but leap to the left until you reach the original decimal point.

1. $0.00000034 = 3.4 \times 10^{-7}$

2. $0.006 = 6.0 \times 10^{-3}$

Hint Leave scientific notation to the mathematicians. It is rather pretentious to say that your Rolex watch cost £4.5×10^3.

CHAPTER 65

A Light Year

A light year is the distance that light travels in one year. Now light travels at 300 000 km (or 300 000 ÷ 8 and × 5 = 187 500 miles) per second. (Or, for the purist, more exactly 299 792.458 km per second.) Now let's be clear about this. In one second, in the mere blink of an eye, light travels 300 000 km!

Astronomers work with very large numbers so they measure distance in light years. That is how far light travels not in one second, not in one day, but in one year! So 1 light year is 300 000 × 60 × 60 × 24 × 365 km which is 9.46 million million km or in scientific notation 9.46×10^{12} km.

Alpha Centauri is the nearest star system to our own solar system.

It's only 4 light years away!

CHAPTER 66

Albert Einstein

(1879–1955)

$\mathbb{A}$nd last, but definitely by no means least, the crème de la crème of all mathematicians, Albert Einstein. If ordinary people in the street know nothing else about Einstein, they know he was a genius. 'Who do you think I am? Einstein?' would be the obvious response to being asked, 'What's 195^2, Dad?' (Dad could obtain temporary Einstein status if he reads 'Squares You Can Do in Your Head' earlier in the book.)

Born in Ulm, Germany, Einstein was the son of Jewish parents. Unlike Gauss, von Neumann and many others who were computers on legs before they could toddle, Einstein did not shine in school. He was lazy, especially at subjects which he considered trivial and did not interest him.

But things changed when he became a young man. One moment, Einstein was working in the University of Berlin, finding a few flaws in Isaac Newton's Laws of Gravity, and the next he was in America, the most famous scientist in the world.

If my pupils ever came across $E = mc^2$ it would have been because I had set them an exercise about substituting in a formula where E is Energy measured in joules, m is mass in kilograms, and c is the speed of light in a vacuum. In the world of Einstein, everyone is out of their depth and black holes and the Big Bang are unimaginable concepts. If any budding genius wanted to know more, I always passed the buck to my colleagues in the Physics Department. I was sure they would be delighted to explain everything ... in detail.

Unlike his predecessor, the lonely introverted Isaac Newton, Einstein was a celebrity scientist and he loved it, enjoying his acquaintance with film stars, presidents and the rich and famous. Everyone recognized his picture with the shock of white hair, his wild eyes and his bohemian style clothes.

He even enjoyed his teaching commitments at the university, although he once remarked that in a co-ed situation, it might be difficult for the boys to concentrate with all the beautiful girls in the lecture room. 'No,' said the male pupils, 'we would be listening to you very intently, sir.'

'I don't believe you,' laughed the great man. 'Such boys would not be worth teaching.'

Very early on, Einstein had been able to see where an understanding of his famous formula would lead. He was always a man of peace but he wrote to the president of the United States and urged him to fund research into the development of the atomic bomb. He was concerned that the German Nazis and the Japanese might get there first.

By doing this, Einstein most certainly changed the course of world history.

Postscript

(Well, I didn't expect them to remember everything)

I was having dinner in a restaurant with my golfing chums and the waiter brought me a glass of red wine which I hadn't ordered.

'That's from the gentleman sitting at the far end of the bar, Madam. He says he still remembers that Pythagoras wouldn't eat beans.'